Do I Need Boobs With This Dress?

Do I Need Boobs With This Dress?

Redesigning life
after
breast cancer

Lynne Hanson

Westcom Press
La Quinta, California

Published by Westcom Press, LLC
53605 Avenida Cortez
La Quinta, CA 92253

westcom.press@mac.com
310-406-8300

Printed in the United States of America

Cover and author photographs by
Ronald Flores Photography
www.rfdcphoto.com

Do I Need Boobs With This Dress? is available for bulk purchase at special discounts by corporations, non-profits, institutions, and other organizations. For more information, contact the publisher.

*To all the women dealing with the
emotional and physical scars of breast cancer,
and to those who love them.*

Contents

Prologue

I can do this. After all, I *am* a clothing designer. It's finally time to do it. I'm going to design a line of clothes for women like me—women who have had mastectomies, yet can't have or don't want implants. I can do this.

But first I have to have a dress form with all the deformities and nuances of the scars left from mastectomies. Then I can drape and use the form to create my line. A dress form with boobs just won't work.

I purchase the most flat-chested form that I can find, but it's not flat enough. After measuring and comparing our bodies, I see that our shapes are shockingly different.

Camouflaging the form's breasts by wrapping fabric around them doesn't work. It becomes clear that I have to carve away part of the dress form, mirroring the surgery my doctors performed on me.

I peel off the outer fabric of the dress form, not sure what I will find underneath. Layers and layers of fabric come off until I finally reach a rough fiberglass frame. It's time to cut. I get out all the saws I have in my immense collection. Through the years, I acquired every type of cutting device in existence, from an assortment of tiny X-Acto knives to giant hand saws that any logger would envy, plus the huge radial arm saw in the corner of my garage.

My stomach ties itself up in its all-too-familiar knot when I think of the many saws and knives that must have been used on my body during my multiple surgeries. My nerves tingle like I'm hearing the sound of fingernails on a chalkboard. But I move on.

I start with a small mat cutter and end up using the

sleek triangular handsaw that my sister Jann gave me. It is surprisingly effortless to saw away the tiny breasts. They melt away like butter. It feels wonderful. Cathartic. The saw and I are one, as shards of fiberglass fly around me.

But the form is still not right.

I measure the form's rib cage area, which I have not yet touched. The entire chest area around the missing breasts is not right. My hands slowly compare it with my own chest, recording each and every bump and lump that is left after every semblance of my breasts was removed.

On one side of my chest, the skin is firm. I feel a lump of scar tissue under the scar that goes directly over the flat area where my beautiful breast once sat. Underneath I can feel the uneven hard bone, with a dent in the middle where my nipple had been.

The other side is different. I run my hand over rolls of loose skin which had covered first my breast and then an ill-fated implant. I should get this cleaned up, I think. It's messy, and it's also an unwelcome reminder of a long journey. It's harder to feel the bone underneath, but when I press hard enough, I find me. The side of my chest area, under my arms all the way around to my back, feels unusually bulky. It accentuates the flat shapelessness of my breastless body.

I need to cut away more. Again and again, I saw away at the dress form, measuring the proportions against mine, each time needing to cut away more. How can that be? The surgeon cut away my breasts, not my entire body. The scars extend only across my chest, not down the rib cage. How big could my tiny breasts have really been?

The form's chest starts to look concave, but as I glance down at my chest, I realize that I, too, am concave. I am on the right track, as horrifying as this is.

It's not until most of the chest and rib cage area is carved away that I finally get the right proportions. I am shocked. The massive hole in the dress form goes vertically from just below the collar bone almost to the waist, and horizontally all the way across the front to under the arms.

All this was taken away from my body, I think. *This* is what was taken from me.

I am beginning to understand why women who've had mastectomies need to grieve. We have lost a lot. Not only a big part of what defines our femininity, but a good chunk of ourselves. Although a breast is not a limb, it is not merely an extraneous bump, either. Tucking the floppy little plastic bags they call implants into our bodies does not begin to fill the gaping hole that's left by everything we've lost.

Our bodies have been violated and they need to heal. This takes time, courage, and support.

I realize I need to help other women. I need to help myself. I have not understood this until now. At this moment, it is my obsession.

CHAPTER ONE

I Always Wanted to Have Monica Silverman's Body

I grew up during the fifties and sixties in suburban Maryland just outside Washington DC. It looked like any suburban neighborhood—tree-lined cul-de-sacs with modest red brick ramblers and split-level homes, and the occasional splattering of modest custom homes.

Innovative for its time, the neighborhood had been developed as a co-op, which some on the outside saw as a socialistic experiment. We were the liberals of the time. Our neighborhood was built on an old golf course, and the stately clubhouse was saved and renovated as a community center complete with a community pool. There were acres and acres of community-owned woods for building forts, blazing trails, and riding horses, and a creek with a dam to catch crawfish, tadpoles, and minnows.

It was idyllic suburban freedom at its best. Our socialistic community and the presence of the extraordinary brainpower of many government intellectuals and international dignitaries set us apart from other neighborhoods. Academics and worldliness were valued above almost anything else.

My grandparents had emigrated from Eastern Europe to New York City's impoverished but flavorful Lower East Side. In the forties, my parents, Nee and Sid, left the comfort of

NYC and boldly went where no relative had gone before—Washington, DC. It was a revolt of epic proportions to leave New York, and our relatives were still shocked (how could you possibly leave New York? Are the streets even paved there?).

My father was a civil service employee at the Pentagon. We have yet to figure out exactly what he did, but we have surmised that his life was not that of an ordinary civil servant. My mother was the Supervisor for Special Education for our school district, one of the top school districts in the country. It was unusual for wives in the neighborhood to work outside the home, but the few who did were extraordinary, just like my mother.

Even though my parents worked long hours, I never felt neglected. I was always off playing or drawing something. Like most young girls, I loved horses and became a very accomplished drawer of horses. I also loved to analyze the floor plans of existing homes and create my own designs. When I was ten years old, my desk drawers were filled with architectural drawings of floor plans.

Creative and stubborn, I was not happy with my given name, so in second grade, I asked my mother to please inform my teacher that from now on I was to be called Tzuzi, my version of Suzanne, my middle name. Lynne was far too boring for the likes of me. It didn't stick, but it was indicative of my journey to find my identity.

I was the middle child. Not academic, like the rest of my family, but the imaginative one. My older sister, Jann, whom I hated and worshipped at the same time, loved to argue with people (she ended up in law school) and she'd scare away my friends. But if she told me that the sky was green, I would believe her and defend to my death that the sky was green. My younger sister, Lauren, spent her time making hovercrafts out of vacuum motors and contemplating how to better the world. She was her own person and had no interest in becoming a Jann groupie.

Life was good, except for my never-ending desire to have Monica Silverman's body. She was thin and beautiful, every feature dainty and perfect. Always popular, she was also sophisticated after living in France for two years, as many of my neighbors did. In high school she was both a pom-pom girl and one of the smart kids. Education and brains were valued at our school; it was cool to be smart.

I wasn't known as part of the smart crowd *or* the popular crowd. I kept to myself, and the minute classes let out, I was off to ride my horses or go to swim team practice.

It was the era of Twiggy, and I wanted so badly to be built just like Monica. Unfortunately, my body decided that I was destined for the more curvaceous look. I had real hips and curves, a wider, more substantial body, just like my mother. She commented that we would look great if we spent our lives walking sideways, as we had beautiful profiles with perfectly shaped breasts and flat tummies. But from a straight-on view, we were definitely broad-beamed.

Yet my breasts were *amazing*. They were not too big, not too small, perfectly symmetrical. My mother was against my wearing a bra too soon, perhaps because it'd mean I was not her little girl anymore, so I would steal my older sister's bras. Jann had large breasts, so needless to say, the fit was not ideal. Taken in with safety pins, her bras were constantly coming off or breaking apart during gym class. It was incredibly embarrassing.

My sister finally figured out why all her bras were disappearing, and she took me to the local discount department store to purchase my own. There was no fitter there to help us find the right fit, but we did our best. With my AA cups and wide chest, it was hard to find bras that fit. By the time the bra fit around my chest, the cups were proportionately way too large for my perky little wonder breasts.

I really didn't need a bra for support, but having one was important to me because the peer pressure in the gym locker room after our showers was intense. Everyone was expected to put on a bra while getting dressed. Mine were definitely utilitarian— white cotton or stiff nylon, cheap and simple. It didn't matter what it looked like, what mattered was that I had a bra.

But then something wonderful happened. I went to college in New York City and found a whole new world of braless rebels. It was ironic that I was even at the Parsons School of Design. I had applied when it was known as an elite school for high-end interior designers. In a short time, and unbeknownst to others and me, it had transformed itself to the leading school for a new avant-garde major called *Environmental Design*. The school and the students had no idea what we were doing, but we were going to change the world, one braless hippie at a time. It was a shock for me at first, as I had expected more of a finishing school environment, but I was surprised by how quickly I embraced my unexpected freedom and this new direction.

My preppy dresses and trousers gave way to jeans, which quickly became the staple of my wardrobe. In the more traditional suburbs where I grew up, girls only wore jeans when riding their horses, but now I was able to wear jeans for just about every occasion. Then the bra came off. It was cool at my uber-edgy school go braless. We were the creatives of the world, hippies and changers of the establishment. My bra came off with ease and my unencumbered, beautifully symmetrical breasts were my ticket out of the confinement of a world where I had not belonged.

No matter how tight the top, my perky little breasts were right in front of the world. No bra, no camisole, just my jaunty boobs out there for all to see. With sweaters, they were not even noticed, but in brisk weather with skimpy tops, it was abundantly clear that I was not wearing a bra. Remember the days when showing one's high-spirited little nipples poking through one's clothes was the look? (Or am I showing my age?)

I remained braless as I tired of New York and moved to San Diego, also a bastion of the braless. It was easy in a world of halter tops and tank tops to let my boobies go free. Not until my husband, our girls, and I moved to the Pacific Northwest many years later did bras slowly start to come back into my life. Even after giving in and wearing a bra full time, I was never interested in finding fancy bras. My wide chest and small breasts made it a never-ending challenge just to find bras to fit. Why waste the time and money on something fancier when I really didn't want it the first place?

Even after nursing two children and approaching forty, I loved my breasts. Sure, they could have used a little lift, but they were still great. After all, almost every woman in our society has some sort of body issue, might it be hips, thighs, or arms. My breasts were not one of mine.

CHAPTER TWO

Zipper Number One

My mother was diagnosed with breast cancer, so I started getting annual mammograms when I was just thirty-two. Breast cancer was prevalent in my extended family as well, among the many wonderful ailments that come with being of east European Jewish descent, so I was very conscious of my risk.

The mammogram was always a fun process. The main problem was trying to fit my breasts into the mammography machine. I am only five-foot four, so I had to stand precariously on my toes, trying to keep my balance while my tiny breasts were flattened out between two sheets of Plexiglas.

Since men cherish our breasts so much, why hasn't a man come up with another product, less barbaric than one that puts forty pounds of pressure on one of the most tender parts of a woman's body? And even more puzzling, why hasn't a *woman* come up with something better?

"Hi, sweetie," the technician would chime. "Now, this isn't going to hurt a bit." Really. Did she honestly think I would buy that? I have never understood why other women lie to us like this. Of course it's going to hurt! *You have breasts, too. You know it's going to hurt.*

So, after eight years of annual mammograms, it was not a total surprise when the radiologist found a suspicious cloudy area in my left breast. The doctor ordered an ultrasound, and the results were inconclusive. I was surprisingly calm when he then suggested a lumpectomy. He explained that I could go without one and have another ultrasound at a later date, but I was not comfortable with postponing it. Not with *my* family history. A lumpectomy was the most drastic of my options, but I did not want to leave any doubt as to what this lump was.

I was just 39—far too young to have cancer—so I was not worried. I just wanted to make sure. I was even willing to mutilate my beautiful breasts. Alan, my husband of seventeen years, didn't seem to mind either. The possibility of cancer was too scary to ignore.

I was scheduled for a very early morning outpatient surgery with general anesthesia. Even though I had given birth to two daughters without any painkillers (a decision that was really stupid), I was not one to forgo knock-out drugs. Knock me out and when I wake up, it will be all over. That's preferable to lying on a cold slab, staring up at the stark ceiling, contemplating my fate, listening to the doctors and nurses to whom I am entrusting my precious boobs. No, that was not for me! Knock me out.

Alan was at my side. We had been through a lot together, surviving moves all along the West Coast, trying to avoid the establishment lifestyle, only to end up in Seattle, sucked into the lavish perks of corporate and suburban life.

We had made arrangements for our girls, now ten and eight, to go to friends' houses after school. Both girls were very involved in their activities and I enjoyed driving them to their obsessions. I drove so much that I kept an open bag of coffee beans in the car to keep me awake. I enjoyed the smell, and it created a warm, cozy, home-like feel in the car. Coffee was a very tactile experience for me. Love the smell, the look, the consistency. I love making coffee, love pouring it and the sound that it makes as it hits the bottom of the coffee cup. Hate the taste.

My surgery meant Kelley would miss her ice-skating lessons and Chelsea her basketball practice, but we did not tell them

7

much, just that I had to have a medical procedure and would be home later. After all, this was just a precautionary procedure that would just confirm that all was well.

My exterior was calm as could be, but inside, the thought of the "C" word weighed on my mind. After all, my family and I had always joked that sooner or later our heritage would catch up to one of us. Why shouldn't it be me?

As we silently waited for a nurse to summon us, Alan read a magazine, and I read Alan. It kept my mind off the situation. I studied Alan's round face, his small ski-jump nose scrunched over his graying mustache. His black hair had gray in it, too, and it was starting to thin.

Alan's father was Norwegian, his mother Pacific Northwest Native American (Okanogan), which made for an interesting blend: he was a dark-eyed, curly-haired, small but stocky, Asian-looking Viking. Yes, our kids are Native-American Norwegian Jews.

I thought about our lives together and how we met in San Diego. I'd had enough of the self-important narcissistic students in New York and transferred to school in San Diego to get as far away from them as I could. We met on a school ski trip to Aspen. Yes, I was a hippie, but, in accordance with my contradictory life, I also fell in love with the elite ski resort/mountain sports lifestyle.

Now, in the waiting room, Alan glanced up to see me staring at him. "What?" he asked, but before I could answer, my name was called. I was taken to a private room and asked to change into every patient's favorite garment—the infamous blue-and-white patterned examination gown. I didn't understand why this garment was open in the back when they have to get to the boob in the front. Maybe the medical world liked to make us so uncomfortable that we wouldn't worry about the surgery. It never occurred to me that I was wearing it wrong.

"Hey, darling," the pudgy, fifties-something nurse said, grinning. One of my pet peeves is a stranger calling me endearing names like "darling." *I don't know you, and I'm not your darling.*

"Sweetie," she continued, "you need to change your dressing gown so that it opens in the front." The annoyance of her sweeties and darlings kept my mind off the situation. But not for long.

Oh, boy. Not only would I have the humiliation of the mammogram machine, again, but I had to remove my dressing gown in front of the uber-cheery technician. Why is it called a dressing gown anyway? Are we dressing up or down?

The first order of business was for the technicians to locate the lump by taking a mammogram. As I stood on my tiptoes, hanging onto the damn machine, my breast clamped between the Plexiglas sheets, they would first locate the suspicious area. Then, while I was still fully awake and hanging onto the machine, they'd stick a wire into my breast to pinpoint exactly where the lump was for the surgeon.

I do not like needles, so usually when I get a shot I look away and pinch my neck to distract myself from the needle prick. I did that, although I cannot tell you how in the world I managed while hanging on to that machine. Surprisingly, it didn't hurt when they stuck the wire into my breast.

They freed my breast from the torture machine, and I stood there, at first just impressed with the proficiency of the technician, but then gradually wondering how I would know if she got the right area.

Then it hit me. There was a wire sticking out of my breast. *There's a wire sticking out of my breast!* The room started swirling, and I began to slump to the floor. The technicians caught me and gently sat me in a nearby chair. I guess this happens all the time; there was another wooden chair alongside me, ready to catch the next patient.

"Okay, honey, you just sit yourself down here." Nurse Sweetcakes's dyed brownish hair brushed across my shoulder. It was a color that said, I am not red, I am not brown, I am not gray, I am not anything. I hate that color.

It is one of the stranger sights to look down and see a wire protruding from one's breast. No blood, no redness, no nothing—just a long straight wire sticking out about six inches. It was dark and made from a few thin wires twisted together, like trash bag twisty ties. Not pretty. A colorful one might have been nicer. You could pick your own color, just as you can pick your cast color when you break an arm. I would have gone for some loud, happy color, or maybe a few different colors to make an interesting design in the twist.

I sat on the chair for a while, my head between my legs, trying not to pass out or throw up. I am not good with nausea, and I am a real weenie about it. But I'd never fainted, and I was not about to start. I was determined to be strong, so I gathered myself together, sat in a wheelchair, and let the nurse push me to my room to wait for the lumpectomy. Just do as I'm told and don't think. I didn't even think about the girls, the possibility of cancer, or anything. I just went through the motions of breathing.

Alan was waiting in the room, his dark eyes fixated on a TV screen bigger than we had at home. He looked like he was in heaven. I doubt he saw the wire, which was sticking out between the ties of my blue-and-white gown. Sexy.

"Okay, sweetie, we'll just leave you here until you feel better." My not-so-favorite nurse left us alone.

"What are you watching?" I asked Alan. By now the adrenaline rush had worn off and I was exhausted.

"The People's Court."

"What's that?"

"It's a show about people suing each other, and the judge is the cutest guy."

There it was, the start of my obsession with judge shows.

Alan was not really watching it, though, and neither was I. The noise of the TV allowed us to be left to our own thoughts and fears, pondering the uncertain future in solitude. The idea that something might be wrong seemed unimaginable. I was way too young.

"What are you drinking?" I asked after some time.

"I think they meant it to be coffee."

"Oh."

We returned to our silence. He was right. Judge Wapner was adorable.

After what seemed an eternity, a teenage aide, probably checking out her nursing career options, showed up with a gurney to wheel me into surgery.

"Enjoy *Judge Wapner*."

Alan gave me a kiss and a loving but worried nod.

As we rolled down the long hallways, I was sure everyone was staring at my wire. I did not want to look at anyone and hated staring up at the ceiling. The wheels of the gurney squeaked. My eyes glazed over, and I tried to ignore my discomfort and let my mind wander. For some inexplicable reason, when my mind wants to wander I go to the 1950s TV show, *The Mouseketeers*. I see the young, effervescent, all-American kids with their Mickey Mouse hats, singing and dancing without a care. I wonder what a psychiatrist would think about that.

The aide took me to the prep room, a sterile room with white tile walls, flimsy curtains to give the semblance of privacy with obtuse designs that made no sense (for kicks I try to find the repeat in patterns), sterile metal beds, and the background hum of doctors, nurses, and medical equipment in use. I was lined up alongside other ladies on gurneys, all of us fully conscious, awaiting unknown diagnoses and fates. Lambs lined up for the slaughter. We did not talk. We were too far away from each other to have any conversation, much less an intimate one about breasts and wires.

We were all given IVs and hair caps to go with our beautiful gowns. The nurses and aides were great, checking on us and making sure we were warm and as comfortable as possible. Every time we were moved, our wristbands were checked to make sure we were who we needed to be. That gave me a small inkling of reassurance that a lump and my wire would be the only things removed from my body.

"Hey, cookie." Nurse Sweetcakes put a warm blanket over me and gave me a gentle pat on my thigh. I could smell her Juicy Fruit gum. It made me nauseated. "You just wait here. Let us know if you need anything, and we'll be back to get you as soon as the doctor is ready." It seemed like an eternity.

When it was my turn, I was wheeled into a surgery room, which was nothing like the rooms on *Grey's Anatomy* or *ER*. It was tiny, with few machines and many people, and it was colder than Alaska (my kind of weather!). My surgeon, Dr. Williams, and I had already bonded over tales of the great outdoors, comparing skiing and white-water-rafting trips in Jackson Hole, Wyoming, and Utah. I hear that lots of women develop crushes on their doctors, and I was no exception. He was handsome, compassionate, and about to cut my breast open. How romantic.

"Ready?" he asked me. I could not see his thick brown hair or sparkly eyes under his cap and mask.

"Sure, let's do it."

And the next thing I knew, I was opening my eyes in the recovery room to a whopper of a headache. I groaned, "Where's Alan?" At least I remembered his name. Nurse Sweetcakes noticed me talking to myself.

"He's waiting for you in your room, darling, watching TV."

At that point, I guess she could call me darling. She could call me anything she wanted.

They rolled me up to my room, where Alan had moved on to the TV news, and waited for the anesthesia to wear off. I had a huge bandage across my chest. The anesthesia made me incredibly nauseated, and the bedpan became my new best friend. Alan had been on ski patrol for many years and had seen many injuries, so blood and vomit did not faze him. He just went with the flow. They discharged me within a few hours of my procedure, after I had regained more consciousness and hadn't thrown up for an hour.

My scar was about four inches long and ran across the top portion of my breast. I wondered why Dr. Williams had chosen to put the scar there, where it would be easy to see when I wore low-cut clothing. It did not occur to me at the time that it made the most sense to cut there, because it was the most direct way to the lump. Dr. Williams was not a plastic surgeon. He was just doing his job, but there it was, my first of many scars.

After a few weeks, the swelling went down, and there was a small dent in my beautiful breast just below the slightly raised red scar, which sort of looked like a large zipper. I did not see the need to make such a big statement, none the less, put it on the top of my breast rather than the bottom, but there it was, and I would live with it. No more sexy V-necks for me. The assurance that there was no cancer was by far worth the dent and scar on my perfect breasts. It was over.

13

CHAPTER THREE

Unzipped

I moved on from the surgery and was back to my world, without a thought that the outcome could be cancer. My parents came to visit, and as always, we had a great time together. They were the best grandparents anyone could ask for, and Alan and my father had an extremely close bond, in part because they shared many interests and in part because Alan was not very close to his parents, so my father had in effect become Alan's father.

My parents had recently retired from their careers in DC and moved to San Diego, where my father kept busy with tennis and my mother with her belly dancing and TV production classes. Mom even started a new career in TV news broadcasting, and eventually won two Emmys for her work coproducing documentaries.

It was a long weekend, and Alan had gone mountain climbing with his cousin Jon in the nearby Cascades. Jon was an even more accomplished climber than Alan, which was saying a lot considering Alan's outdoor obsessions—skiing, mountain climbing, fly-fishing, you name it. With his climbing buddies, Alan would climb a mountain carrying his skis, then ski down it. When we lived in Portland, Oregon, one of his friends commented after a pre-dawn climb of Mt. Hood, "Having fun with Alan means it has to hurt." So true.

Skiing was an activity he shared with the girls, too. In fact,

Kelley and Chelsea were skiing before they could walk. At fifteen months, Kelley would squeal with delight as Alan skied down a hill with her on his shoulders. He would go over small jumps and her face would light up while mine went gray with fear.

In Seattle, he had become obsessed with fly-fishing, and he, Kelley, and Chelsea would religiously watch the TV show *Fishing the West* with their official *Fishing the West* baseball hats firmly on their heads. Both girls had their own fly-tying equipment and loved to experiment with the colorful threads and feathers that Alan had collected.

He would take them out on our drift boat, a bright yellow boat we named the Bumble Bee, designed for floating down shallow rivers while they did catch-and-release fly fishing. I would drive them to a launching point and they, along with our dog, Beans, would climb into the boat and drift off for me to pick them up farther downstream. The serenity of the river, forests, and mountains was their bonding time. It was also my alone time, which I greatly appreciated.

While Alan and Jon were away that Friday, the rest of us headed to the mall. My parents were clotheshorses—my debonair father loved to wear the latest fashion, and my mother loved to buy anything on sale.

"Here, you'll love this," my mother said as she shoved a shirt within inches of my face. I hated it when my mother said this. How did she know what I would love?. She was always buying me clothes I didn't want. They all looked like they were the dregs of the sale rack. "And I got it on sale."

"Thanks, but it's really not me," I told her, trying not to hurt her feelings.

"No, it's you. It's exactly what you wear." Her slightly antiqued face was more determined than ever. She eyed my baggy sweats and oversized T-shirt. "And you don't have to iron it."

She had me there. I hated ironing and avoided it like the plague. But I hated this shirt too. It was beyond huge, with pale pink and white pinstripes. I never wore pink. The pocket on the left side had an embroidered design on it, like a family crest, but I don't think it meant anything. Another clothing company trying to create a snobby image.

I had designed clothes for companies such as Pendleton Woolen Mills and White Stag, yet I was like the cobbler who had holes in her shoes. Though I was always aware of the latest fashions, and sometimes willing to try them, I would inevitably return to my comfort zone of jeans, sweats, and tees. The hippie style of dressing I honed in New York City still dominated my style. After all, my life consisted of carpools and grocery stores and I was not concerned with how the skating moms and the grocery checkout clerks saw me. I wanted to spend my time creating. Although I was a stay-at-home mom, I always had some sort of sideline business relating to my clothing-design background.

Unfortunately, we lived in an environment where image was everything. My artistic nature did not allow me to conform. I was more impressed by the millionaire who wore hard-earned holes in his jeans than the overnight success who had to prove his worth by wearing expensive fashion.

Alan didn't agree. He had always been a competitive person and now was a successful businessman. He expected his family to excel in everything, including the way we'd fit in and reflect his success. He would have been so much happier if I looked like all the other upper-middle-class Seattle housewives.

"I'd just like for you to have a normal nine-to-five job and wear corporate suits," he would tell me in a heated moment.

"Not going to happen," I'd inform him. But it hurt.. When we'd first met, after I'd gone out on a limb and joined the ski club at college, he was attracted to me because I was different from the other girls. I had dark brown hair, cut in a shag style, not the straight sun-bleached blonde hair of the tanned California girls. I wore jeans and T-shirts, not bikini tops and short shorts.

16

So why would he want me to conform now? After all, he was attracted to me *because* I was different.

We had both changed and grown. He wanted to keep up with the Jones and although I tried, it was just not in my DNA. I'd wear pearls, but with overalls, not a suit. I'd collect empty refrigerator boxes for the kids to decorate and play with, not the latest Barbie house. The obvious fact that the neighborhood kids preferred the refrigerator boxes reinforced my determination to not just blend in.

Where he stayed the same and I had changed was in our leisure activities. He was still obsessed with backpacking, mountain climbing, skiing, fishing—everything outdoors— and I'd had enough of it. The comment his friend made that fun with Alan meant it had to hurt was all too true. It seemed like every time we went out we fell into some natural disaster— we got caught in an ice storm, got lost in some isolated ravine, or something equally drastic happened.

It became a joke, but I was done. I'm sure Alan was as hurt by my unwillingness to participate in his activities as I was by his wish for me to conform and fit into suburbia.

At times, I mourned the alternate future we might have had if we hadn't succumbed to the lure of the comfortable suburban life, if we had stuck to our original plan when we were young, idealistic, and anti-materialistic. But I did love my house. It had all the nuances and rooms in the right places I had imagined in the designs I'd drawn as a child.

When we returned from the mall, I stuck the pink shirt my mom had bought into the back of my closet, then collapsed onto the couch, exhausted. I saw a message on my answering machine from Dr. Williams's office, but I assumed it was a courtesy call to let me know that the lump was fine. It was already late in the day, so I would call back on Monday.

Saturday we returned to yet another voicemail, this one from Dr. Williams himself. What a nice guy. My doctor, my crush, calling me over the weekend to assure me that all is well. I tried calling back, and we began a game of telephone tag. Not to worry. We would talk on Monday.

Early Sunday evening, I came home from a day out on my own. The girls were playing with friends, and my parents were in the family room watching television. They told me that Dr. Williams had called again and would like me to call him at home. I called his home and finally caught him.

"Hi, Dr. Williams. Are you getting ready for your Jackson Hole trip?"

He was very calm. He had clearly done this many times. "The lump was fine. There was no sign of any cancer."

I sighed and was about to thank him for going out of his way to call me over the weekend, when he continued, "We did find cancer cells in the milk ducts surrounding the lump."

Pause.

"It's called ductal carcinoma in situ."

Okay . . . .

I guess he thought that would mean something to me. Later I learned that *in situ* is Latin for "in its original place," and *carcinoma*, also Latin, referred to the most common type of cancer, which begins in our tissues. Thanks for that information, Mom, the research queen.

"The lump in question turned out to be fatty tissue," he continued. "But as a precaution, we took some of the tissue from around the lump, and inside the milk ducts we found ten cancerous cells, just one less than it would take to officially call it cancer, but enough to call it pre-cancer."

We all have precancerous cells in our bodies, and usually they are naturally killed off. But sometimes they multiply and become cancerous.

Silence.

I walked to the front of the house, toward the staircase off to one side of the spacious entryway. Feeling very heavy, I sat down, hard, on the third step.

"We have options," Dr. Williams went on. "You could wait

18

and do nothing, getting mammograms often, hoping to catch any problems. You could have more ultrasounds and watch the area closely. You could have radiation and monitor the breast after the rounds of radiation. Or you could have another lumpectomy to see if there are more cancer cells in the area."

So, this was intense. I started playing with my hair, concentrating on the wavy brown strands, a habit that usually comforted me. My eyes fixated on the striations of wood on the stairs.

Suddenly, there was a loud commotion at the front door.

"Hey, honey, we're home," Alan crooned in a sing-song voice as he and Jon banged at the door. "Come kiss me. I'm really gross from the mountain. I don't have keys. Let us in."

They were clearly a few beers in and way too happy.

"Let us in!" they yelled in harmony.

I jerked the door open, gave them the nastiest look I could, then walked away to continue talking to Dr. Williams. As I turned away, my arm went out to stop them from coming toward me. I wanted to slam the door in their grinning, filthy faces. Alan and Jon followed me to the stairs.

"Go away," I mouthed, glaring. "I have cancer."

Alan tilted his head, his eyebrows furrowed. The left eyebrow with the childhood scar scrunched more than the other, making an oddly curved line. I motioned for them to disappear, and he and Jon tiptoed into the family room.

To add insult to injury, apparently Dr. Williams had spoken to my parents earlier in the day and had alluded to the results. His confidentiality breach did not faze me, but I was furious with my parents. Dr. Williams and I decided to continue our discussion on Monday, and I stormed into the family room.

"Why didn't you tell me?"

My father took control, as he always did. "We didn't know everything, so we wanted Dr. Williams to tell you. All we knew was that there was a problem." He was trying to stay calm, trying to diffuse the conversation, but he could tell I was not buying it.

19

I was angry. Angry at my parents for not preparing me. Angry at Alan for coming home so happy. And angry at my perfect breasts for betraying me.

At that moment I knew my fate. I would go through the motions of doing my due diligence, researching as much as I could. (Let me rephrase that: My *mother* and I would research as much as we could.) My mother, the research queen, the scientist (her undergraduate degree was in biology), and the matriarch of our family's cancer history. We discussed cancer all the time, so I knew that when it was my turn, I would handle it as aggressively as she did.

There was no question of what to do. The choice was a simple one for me. Find out if there was more cancer. Have another lumpectomy, where they would take more of the tissue surrounding the suspicious area. I was not going to take any chances; cancer was inevitable for me, and I had a wonderful life and family that I was not about to lose.

The second time around was not as eventful as the first. All Dr. Williams had to do was unzip the zipper and take out more stuffing. Luckily, no wire would be involved, as my ever-present scar led the way to the area in question..

A second surgery in one month and a future with cancer. I was way too young for this. My fortieth birthday was coming up, and I was determined not to let cancer mar my celebration of the start of a new decade.

CHAPTER FOUR

Mountain or Molehill

Second lumpectomy done. We knew the routine. Dr. Williams phoned me with the test results: They didn't find any more cancer cells. What a relief. The problem I faced was how to handle the information I had. Yes, my body had produced cancer cells. Yes, they were found in the milk ducts, a common area for breast cancer. Yes, my family history was riddled with breast cancer. But officially, this was pre-cancer, not cancer. And, might I add, I now had a giant dent in my perfect breasts.

My mother and I had discussed cancer ad nauseum. She had breast cancer at the age of fifty-one. She participated in a study at NIH, where she had a double mastectomy with reconstruction. She loved to talk about her tests and her appointments with her doctors, and she always reminded me how diligent I needed to be. She took me to classes on how to discover suspicious lumps, sent me articles about breast cancer, and shared way too much information of how my father discovered the lump in her breast.

Luckily, her cancer never returned but her implants became hard as rocks and impossible to remove. Later she had a rare form of cancer in her fallopian tube, which was removed with a complete recovery. Skin cancer was ever-present, but she was diligent about having it removed. She knew cancer and made sure that I did too.

I phoned the NIH to see if there were any research programs I could join. Unfortunately, the funding for such programs had taken a hit as the economy worsened, and there were no studies to fit my situation. So I was back to my own research, with the help of my mother, the support of friends and family, and many, many second opinions.

"I'm giving you the award for getting the most second opinions," Dr. Williams informed me. "What have you found?"

"That there is no right answer, no right procedure.

"Dr. X suggests that I do nothing and just monitor my breast with mammograms.

"Dr. Y suggests that I have eight weeks of radiation, which will make me incredibly tired and shrivel my perfect breasts into nothing but hanging skin.

"Dr. Z suggests that I get chemo and *then* radiation, which will melt my entire body into mush."

My relationship with Dr. Williams had evolved from lighthearted conversations about our outdoor adventures to serious business. My second opinions were all over the map. Radiation therapists pushed radiation, and surgeons pushed surgery.

All along, just as with the lumpectomies, I knew what I had to do. I was simply going through the motions to show Alan that it was the right decision for me. With my family history, a family that needed me (and I needed them), and my beautiful breast already scarred, this was a no-brainer.

I would have a full mastectomy with immediate reconstruction just like my mother, and I would have it as soon as possible. I wanted any sign of cancer out of me, and I wanted it out of me fast. Right then. All they had to do was unzip the zipper that had been unzipped twice already. Easy.

Alan noted that a mastectomy seemed like overkill, but he would support and love me no matter what I decided. I knew that.

I had to find a plastic surgeon to perform the reconstruction.

My HMO allowed me to use any surgeon I wanted, even outside its organization. I thought that this was unusual, but didn't question it, I loved having that flexibility. Perhaps there was a shortage of plastic surgeons within the HMO.

Again, I earned the award for the most second opinions. I needed to know my options. It seemed perfectly natural to me to over-research, as I am the product of the research queen, but I guess not to the extent that I did.

I had a well-rehearsed spiel.

"It's my fortieth birthday," I would calmly tell each doctor I interviewed. "And I'm having a mastectomy and reconstruction for a birthday present."

I emphasized that it was a present for my fortieth birthday. After all, it was true and I needed that edgy note of sarcasm to get me through this.

It was amusing to see their reactions. They were as varied as the second opinions. Some were stoic; most were just confused. Some would put their hand on my knee with empathy and just stare. By the time I got to Dr. Jacoby, probably number ten, I knew right from the start that he was different. For one thing, we met in his office, not in an examination room, where the other doctors stashed me.

"What can I do for you?" he asked, just like everyone else. He towered over his carved wooden desk as he gently leaned forward.

As soon as he asked, I started crying. I knew he was the one. He did not take pity on me, but he had the warmth and gentle assurance I needed. I was going to be okay in his and Dr. Williams's hands. I was now in love with two doctors.

While I'd recovered from my earlier surgeries, I had grown to appreciate the oversize blouse my mother had given me. It was my comfort shirt, cool, baggy, never needing ironing. The lightweight cotton kept its soft shape without being too stiff.

I was wearing the shirt one afternoon, thinking about the upcoming surgery, when the girls' pet hamster caught my eye. I gently lifted him out of his cage and slipped him into the crested pocket I had always thought so dumb. The button on the pocket closed just enough to keep the little guy comfortably nestled. He seemed very happy in his little den, traveling around with me. He would move around, fall asleep, wake up, and move around some more.

I began carrying him around regularly, pointing to the moving pocket and say, "See, I have breast cancer."

I was proud of myself, keeping a sense of humor. I really did have this tangible, alien thing called cancer moving in my body, underneath my big shirt. I thought it was funny, but other people did not. The joke was usually met with uncomfortable silence. Alan was speechless at first. Then he suggested that maybe I should see a therapist.

He was doing his best to help me, but humor was how I handled it. I was doing what I needed to do.

CHAPTER FIVE

Decorating 101

When we lived in Portland during my mid-twenties, I worked at Pendleton Woolen Mills, where I met Karren, a fabric designer. She was the West Coast version of Monica Silverman. She had a fantastic lean body and wore cool denim skirts and Frye boots. I hoped to someday have a pair of those boots myself, and I added them to my list of future aspirational purchases.

We began having lunch together, and our friendship progressed to hanging out socially. Karren and her husband celebrated Alan's thirtieth birthday with us, showing up at our tiny apartment in their little red Aston Martin with a six-pack of beer.

I wanted to be her when I grew up.

When she told me she was pregnant, I was very happy for her but concerned that this new friendship was fleeting. At the time, I had no desire to be around babies. My career was my focus. But we continued to get together with them, and after Karren gave birth, we showed up at their house, unannounced, right after she got home from the hospital. We'd brought a rubber tree plant. For a newborn.

Somehow, neither a baby nor a poisonous plant would stand in the way of our friendship, which only continued to grow. Our families even lived together for a time while she was going through a tough divorce.

Now, more than a decade later, our friendship was as strong as ever despite the distance. She was living in Salt Lake City, her hometown, had remarried, and had another daughter. Throughout the years, our families had gotten together for various outdoor adventures—skiing, hiking, canoeing, white-water rafting—in Salt Lake and in Jackson Hole, Wyoming, where they had a condo. During part of those holidays, Karren and I would catch up while Alan took all the kids exploring the wilderness of Wyoming and Utah. When Karren's middle boy was asked in fourth grade to write a paper on a famous explorer, he wrote about Alan.

We also spent most of my birthdays together, and this year would be no exception. She was bringing her youngest daughter, four-year-old Aubri.

As soon as they walked in the front door, Karren insisted on seeing our bedroom. "When we talk on the phone while you're recovering after your surgery, I need to picture your surroundings." She removed the ever-present pencil from behind her ear, where it had been stationed for the fourteen-hour drive. "We need to decorate your bedroom so I can see you in a beautiful place." Aubri followed in step with Karren, fingering her mother's pleated shorts, which had replaced the denim skirts Karren used to wear. She still wore the Frye boots.

I was certainly not opposed to having a beautiful Karren-decorated bedroom.

"I know exactly what you need," she said. "This room is big, and it needs some pattern and color. You've done a great job with the paint color, a typical Lynne 'non-color,'" she laughed, referring to the warm-grayish walls.

Neutral non-colors were usually more my style in clothing, not in paint choices. My living room was a deep periwinkle, the dining room was coral, and my family room was a deep blue-green, with different patterns of wallpaper. The girls had followed suit. Kelley had chosen red for her bedroom door and green for her room. Her bathroom was red, chartreuse, and peach. Chelsea had chosen purple for her room, and the playroom was chartreuse and turquoise.

When I finished painting the living room, a neighbor dropped by just to see what color I had chosen.

"Heard you'd done it again," she said.

By now I had a reputation to uphold.

The neutral of the bedroom had come about quite by accident. We had an abundance of almost-empty paint cans in the garage—greens, yellows, reds and blues from all of the other rooms. I decided, just for the heck of it, to combine all the various leftovers.

House paint is a fascinating substance. The base color, usually some sort of white, can only absorb so much added coloring. At a certain point, it reaches its limit and turns a beautiful taupe-ish neutral. This was my neutral, I find it to be the most soothing, chameleon-like color, as it goes with everything. I now use it often.

Karren continued to examine my bedroom, occasionally pausing to jot down notes. "We can move the bed in front of the fireplace you never use, and the mantle will make the perfect headboard," she said. "There's a great Ralph Lauren sheet pattern with rich jewel-toned colors that we can cut up and sew for curtains, tablecloths, and pillow shams."

It was not in our DNA to go out and buy fabric to make curtains. Anything we did had to be created from something it was not.

Karren worked diligently cutting the sheets, matching the patterns, and making the perfect curtains, tablecloths, and shams anyone could ever imagine. I made the meals and the all-important coffee, which Karren inhaled. Otherwise, I just sat on the floor next to her, talking about everything except the surgery. When we got together, we solved the problems of the world, so during this visit, we solved every problem but mine. It felt good to solve problems other than mine.

Karren and I rearranged the bedroom furniture a few times to find the ideal setup. "This is where your friends can sit as they talk to you," Karren said once she'd figured it all out. "This is where the kids can play or read while they spend time with you. And this is where you can prop yourself up while watching your judge shows."

She had my life completely worked out in this room. In her mind, my life would exist only in here, the space she had lovingly created.

CHAPTER SIX

Just Another Zipper

With the bedroom fully Karren-decorated, I was ready for surgery. Dr. Jacoby coordinated with Dr. Williams and all was in place. I arranged for Kelley and Chelsea to go to friends' houses for a few days while I was in the hospital, and my parents to visit a week after I got home. I don't like to be around people when I don't feel well, but I knew having the girls at home would be nice. I could occasionally visit with them yet they'd be focused on their own lives. I'd delayed my parents' visit because I didn't want my mother at my house with nothing to do but dote on me. After all, I was *just* removing a breast. No biggie, I told myself.

Friends reached out to help in any way they could. Our social circle was young, so I was the first to encounter the dreaded "C" word. We were all setting precedence for those who would unfortunately and inevitably follow.

It was up to Dr. Jacoby to determine if he would do immediate reconstruction or wait, based on how the breast looked after Dr. Williams did his thing. This was my third surgery in one month. To me, it was inconceivable that I would have to wait for reconstruction and go through another operation. I made it clear that I preferred immediate reconstruction.

Dr. Williams unzipped the zipper and removed every bit of

the breast tissue, including the nipple and skin around it. In my vast research, I read that the nipple is one of the most common places for cancer to start. If I was going to the trouble of having a mastectomy, I wanted any chance of cancer out of my body.

The mastectomy went well, and Dr. Jacoby took over in the operating room, positioning my new implant under the chest muscle. At this point, the implant just had a bit of saline in it, so it was almost flat. A tube went under my skin from the implant to just under my armpit, where it was attached to a small valve. All you could see and feel of the valve was a bump in the skin, about one inch in diameter. The bump was actually a little round receptacle resembling the plastic squeaky balloon inside a dog's squeaky toy.

The idea was to add saline and gradually pump up the implant under the chest muscle and stretch the muscle and skin. The concept is barbaric but it creates the most natural-looking breast. The skin is expanded to about twice the size of the desired breast, it's left that way for a while to permanently stretch the skin, and then half of the saline is removed along with the tube and valve. The theory is that stretching the skin and then removing the cause of the stretch creates the breast's ideal "proper droop."

The surgery went flawlessly, and, with the exception of my usual throw-up routine, my recovery was uneventful. A large bandage across my chest allowed me to avoid my reality. I returned home on schedule and my beautiful room was ready for me. All was in place.

Five days after surgery my mother called and said that they were, for some unexplained reason, changing their plans and coming early. They had an evening flight, so Alan planned to pick them up on his way home from work. It was okay for them to come early, as I was feeling almost human. I even cleaned up a bit, moving some lightweight things around. I tired easily, which was expected, but as the day progressed, searing pain began to take over.

30

I was alone and began to panic. As the oddball "creative" in my neighborhood of beautiful housewives, I was not terribly close to anyone—except my friend Brenda, who also did not fit in. Along with our family's rescue dog, Beans, she was my morning walking buddy.

"Hi, could . . . could you come over . . . *now?*"

"What's wrong?" she asked, trying to sound calm.

"I don't know, but I hurt so badly."

"I'll be right up. Mandy is here. I'll bring her." Mandy was her teenage daughter.

I unlocked the front door and went back to my bed, where I curled up in pain. I could not breathe. All I could do was cry and try to find a comfortable position. Even the beautiful bedding and curtains could not calm me.

Brenda let herself in.

"I don't know what happened," I tried to say, but my voice was hovering on hysteria.

Brenda found a paper lunch bag in the kitchen and had me blow into it to help me calm down and breathe. Slowly, I was able to stop crying. Mandy stood at the end of the bed, frozen, watching this crazy adult thrash in pain.

"I'll call Alan," Brenda said.

Alan got home quickly, slamming the door from the garage into the house and running into the bedroom, piercing dark eyes as wide as could be. He undid his tie and threw it and his blazer on the floor. Beans curled into it, looking for a place to hide.

"What's going on?"

Brenda and Mandy stood to one side as he rushed over to me.

I had gained control and was not panicking. The pain was still terrible, but I kept reminding myself that I had just had surgery, and this was probably normal.

"I don't know," I said, "but it hurts so much. It's swollen and hot, but maybe that's normal after surgery. I feel like such a wuss."

None of my extensive research had addressed this. I felt helpless, stupid, wussy, and embarrassed as everyone was staring at me writhing in pain while wearing a short flowery nightgown definitely not made for rolling around. We were perplexed.

Alan's face seemed longer and whiter than normal. He glanced at Brenda, puzzled. "I can't tell what's wrong. What do you want to do?" he asked. "I don't see anything wrong, and you seem better now. I don't want to take you to the hospital if you don't need to go." He was not a fan of hospitals and had seen his fill of them in the past few months.

"Let's call the doctor."

Alan phoned the surgeon's and the plastic surgeon's office. Both offices were closed and the voicemail instructed the caller to call 911. I was *not* about to call 911. Yes, I was in a great deal of pain, but I didn't see it as a life or death matter. We stared at each other until Brenda took control with her schoolteacher authority. "I think you should take her to the hospital, just to be sure. I'll pick up your parents at the airport in case you don't get home in time."

Wrapped in my flannel bathrobe, with my dainty little nighty underneath, we headed to the hospital. Every bump in the road sent excruciating pain through my chest. Alan put his right hand on my leg, driving with his left. He tried to keep his eyes on the road while watching me to make sure I didn't pass out.

The hospital was not yet crowded with Friday night mishaps, and a young intern came to examine me right away.

"What can I do for you?"

"We don't know," Alan began. "She had a mastectomy five days ago, and all of a sudden she's in so much pain, and there seems to be swelling. She did lift some things, but they weren't heavy. We don't know what's going on."

The young intern took a few moments to read the chart. "Well," he said haughtily, "we really can't tell what's happening here. You had an out-of-network plastic surgeon perform the surgery, so how are we supposed to know what is normal for his type of surgery?"

"I can tell you that I'm in a tremendous amount of pain, and the breast is swollen." I tried to be firm, but the pain was getting in the way.

"How can I tell if it's swollen?" he replied. "*Your* surgeon can't use our emergency room, so he can't come here to see you, so how can we tell? We don't have his notes or know what meds you're on, so what can we do for you?"

I was exhausted, Alan was helpless, and neither of us had any answers for this haughty a-hole.

"Can we call in another surgeon?" Alan suggested. He had always been a great mediator, and he saw that we were getting nowhere.

"Well, I just don't see that it will help, as there is no way to tell if your breast size is normal from the surgery or not. You just had surgery. Of course you're in pain. What do you think happens after surgery?" There was not a trace of empathy in his face. "I can't tell if there is a problem because, I repeat, you used an outside surgeon, so I can't see what I can do for you."

Maybe the intern's indignation caused enough frustration to distract me from the pain, but by that point, I just wanted to go home. Alan saw that, and we decided to leave. In hindsight, I wish we had insisted on seeing someone and insisted that they let Dr. Jacoby consult, but I just wanted my bed, a strong dose of painkillers, and my mother.

I climbed into bed, exhausted, in pain, and drugged. Brenda dropped off my parents, and my mother hurried to my room. She did not notice the beautiful new decor. She probably wouldn't have noticed anyway. She was used to me redoing my rooms, changing everything from paint color to furniture—even a room's purpose.

"I knew I needed to be here," she said, stroking my hair. "For some reason, I knew we needed to come now. I just had a sense."

She was not the type to believe in senses in that way, so I was surprised. She could not have been more right. It had been a long time since I'd felt like a little girl who needed her mother. Now I needed to be a child again, comforted by the unconditional love and concern that only parents can give, the reassurance that they will always be there when you need them.

My swollen breast was searing with pain, but the painkillers began to take the edge off. My room was dark. I *felt* dark. I had been stoic throughout this experience, and now I was falling apart. I could not hold it together any longer. I wanted my comfy bed to engulf me. I wanted to stay in this beautiful dark room and stop the pain. I felt defeated.

But I couldn't be. I had two young children and a wonderful husband who needed me. *Just push through the pain,* I told myself.

Dealing with my daughter Kelley's health problems, we had established a mantra for the times she had to endure something painful:

Close your eyes, grit your teeth, and do it.

It was my turn.

CHAPTER SEVEN

Pistachios in the Dark

We never got any resolution on what happened that night. Inside of me I cried non-stop, but outside I was stoic and strong. My bout of panic that night was embarrassing and we never talked about it again. After a few days of resting, the swollen breast subsided and the pain levels decreased. I tried to move on, alone in my dark room, my sanctuary. I spent as much time as I could recovering there, trying not to think about what I had done by removing my entire breast.

The swollen breast was just a blip on the radar of my recovery, I reassured myself. I also kept reminding myself that taking the breast was a no-brainer due to my family history.

All that Chelsea remembers of my surgery and recovery was see me lying in the dark bedroom eating pistachio nuts. I don't remember the pistachios. What I do remember is neighbor after neighbor coming by, as though I was the pope giving my blessing to the ones not yet touched by cancer. I was moved to know that everyone cared, but they would drop by one after another. It was exhausting.

On one of those days, after watching some TV, then reading a bit, I found it hard to get my eyes to focus, so I was starting to doze off when I felt a presence in the room.

I hazily opened one eye.

"Oh, you're awake." It was one of the skating moms.

Kelley's regular ice-skating had gotten both of us involved in the skating world. It was a land of unrealistic Olympic dreams and crazy stage moms. Kelley's long, elegant limbs and delicate features made her the epitome of a classic ballerina when she was ice-skating. She only skated for the love of skating, and she was practically oblivious to the cutthroat competition.

I wished I could have remained oblivious to the woman standing at the end of my bed, holding a plant.

"Uh, I guess I am," I mumbled.

"I brought you this azalea plant," she said, holding it out in front of her. "Well, we got together and bought you this plant. Tina, Sherry, Rachel, and I. We were so concerned about you. It was my idea." She finally realized I wasn't going to sit up and take the plant from her and set it on the dresser. "Kathi wanted to let you know that she would have bought this for you, but she wasn't asked, so it's just from Tina, Sherry, Rachel, and I. Just in case Kathi says anything to you about who bought you the plant. She was pretty mad that she wasn't included, but it's just from us."

Another time I was dozing off when I looked up to see a neighbor I did not know very well staring down at me. She was also holding an azalea plant. What was it with the azaleas?

Azaleas or not, it was amazingly comforting and surprising that the neighbors rallied around me with such love and support. When we moved in, there was an outpouring of welcome from our neighbors, but as time went by, it was clear that we were the hippies, nature lovers, and perhaps the Beverly Hills Clampetts of the neighborhood.

I received many phone calls, including several from a local cancer support group. A representative wanted to come over to tell me about all the wonderful services her organization provided. I'm just not a joiner. *I was kicked out of Girl Scouts because I skipped too many meetings. I skipped classes in school.*

Support groups are especially distasteful, and I even find them depressing. I was kicked out of a couples support group for calling bullshit on one particularly narcissistic woman. We all have issues, but our problems are insignificant to what is going on in the rest of the world.

I asked the support group lady to *please* not visit, but she would not listen. I tried to explain that my amazing family and friends give me all the support that I needed. We had the same conversation every time she called, and she called often. My mother and I continued to assure her that we were fine. The woman would not have it.

One day, she showed up on my doorstep, unannounced. If she had truly understood what I was going through, she would not have done this. How could she come unannounced and unwanted? In a moment of weakness, my mother let her in.

She had brought a basket of flowers, information on support groups, brochures on the latest mastectomy-related products, and a much-too-happy grin on her face. I had grown to despise much-too-happy people.

"Here we have a lovely brochure about the latest sleeping bra," she chirped. "It's really helpful for the large-breasted woman."

Yes, I'm wearing a baggy T-shirt, but please, lady, how can you not see that I am far from large-breasted? At least give me products I can use!

I was having a hard time with nausea, so I was up and down, rushing to the bathroom constantly. I thought this would be enough to dissuade her from staying, but not a chance. Each time I returned to her relentless enthusiasm and concern. My mother and I finally convinced her that she had done her job and could leave.

Big Brother of the cancer world must have sent a message to everyone about my surgery. I continued to receive calls from support groups, as well as various cancer organizations and institutes. The Fred Hutchinson Cancer Research Center called to ask if I would participate in a cancer research study. As the child of the Olympians of medical research participation, I agreed.

Two women came to my house with a list of questions. I was not feeling well. I wanted them gone.

"When you were eight, what was your diet?"

Really? Was this *really* what they wanted me to remember? Right now? Right after the most painful and emotional surgery of my life? I could not tell you what I ate an hour ago, let alone what I ate as an eight-year-old.

"I liked butter. Cooked peas with butter." That sounded really good to me right then.

They wrote it down.

"My mother had cancer, and many aunts and cousins have had cancer," I volunteered.

They did not write that down.

The remaining questions were pretty much the same. This was for the birds. I was surprised, because Fred Hutchinson is known to be one of the best research centers, and these questions were ridiculous. Honestly, do you remember what you ate as a child? I mean, I remember various foods, but do I remember enough to make it a valid representation of what I ate? Probably not.

I received a summary of their conclusions, which were basically that I had cancer because I had eaten too much fat as an eight-year-old. Not that nearly every female member of my extended family has had breast cancer. No. *I ate too much fat as an eight-year-old.* I will admit that my diet as a child and an adult might have been a factor, but it certainly was not the only cause! My faith in medical studies was seriously wounded.

Soon my notoriety in the neighborhood wore off, and everyone went back to their lives. But then a neighbor brought over a chicken casserole that changed my life. It was sheer ambrosia. In my baggy pajamas, I would stand in front of the sink, looking across the backyard at the distant Olympic Mountain's never-melting glaciers, glimmering in the sunshine. With the largest spoon available, I would inhale pure edible comfort straight out of the cold casserole dish. The comforting smooth texture of the creamy sauce combined with the spectacular view enveloped me in a bubble of calmness in what had become an uncertain world. Later I asked for the recipe, and to this day, the casserole is our family's comfort food.

If I learned anything from this experience, it's that one of the best things you can do for people going through a crisis is to think of them *after* the commotion has died down. That is when they need you the most.

CHAPTER EIGHT

Waking My Inner Dolly Parton

The recovery seemed to take forever. I could not understand why I was having so much trouble getting back to normal life. Every ten days, I'd go to Dr. Jacoby's office for more saline solution to be injected into my chest through the handy underarm valve, and it'd travel through the tube to the implant bag behind my chest muscle.

This was my Arnold Schwarzenegger "I will pump you up" period.

Sounds easy and logical, right?

Not really. First we have the pain of having an implant placed under your stretched chest muscle and freshly scarred skin, a tube running inside your body and a dog's squeaky toy under your arm. And this isn't the tough part. The tough part is the pain every time I went to get pumped up. While the actual injection didn't hurt, the pain returned as the skin and muscle were stretched to create a breast. *Of course it hurts,* I told myself. Muscle and skin that had only recently been cut open was being tormented.

Arnold Schwarzenegger meets Dolly Parton. Because the implant had to be blown up to double its permanent size, I was really bosomy for the first time in my life. I had to put rolled up panty hose on the other side so that I didn't look lopsided. My ballooned breast was growing so large, the skin was stretched like a pregnant belly. Finally I started using socks instead of panty hose to match the size.

40

After each injection, I would spend the next few days in bed on painkillers. It did not make sense to me that I could not handle the pain. Did all women have so much pain? After all, I had given birth to two children without any drugs at all; I was woman! This was worse, though.

For eight months I went through this routine: saline injection, three days in bed, constant pain for a week. I developed what I called my 4 P.M. headaches. Every day, at 4 P.M. Pacific time, rain or shine, summer or winter, I got an excruciating headache. Of course, this coincided with carpool time, but I was not about to let anything get in the way of carpool. That was my chance to see my girls interact with their friends, to have fun with them and eavesdrop on their lives. I learned so much about them during that time.

I became depressed. I had battled depression before and had briefly taken antidepressants, but now I was trying to stay off them. I told myself I was too tough for that. I could manage it myself. And what in the world did I have to be depressed about? Other women had gone through this. I could not understand why I was having such a hard time. Painkillers helped, but as much as I wanted to become an addict, I had a reaction to every painkiller I took for more than three consecutive days. I tried going without painkillers, rotating painkillers, but nothing seemed to help.

Finally, after eight months of hell, my breast looked fantastic. Size A to size C since I had been pumped up to twice the size of the other breast. The pumped-up breast needed to remain that size for some time to stretch the skin. Eventually, my doctor would remove some of the saline so that the skin and breast would match my remaining breast and have its "proper droop." After all, everyone needs proper droop.

After the deflation, the valve was removed, and then Dr. Jacoby created a nipple by folding some skin into a nipple shape and tattooing the area around the nipple. Voilà—my breast was beautiful.

There were certainly other types of implants and other ways to reconstruct a breast, but this made for the most natural looking breast. And it certainly did! I told Dr. Jacoby that when he tattooed my nipple, the least he could do was tattoo a rose or something cool. He disappointed me when he said that he would not do it. He explained that he wasn't a tattoo artist. True, he wasn't a tattoo artist, but he was an artist, nonetheless. He had created a masterpiece with my new breast and, as an artist, I wanted to salute his work with a tattoo. I wanted color on my body to bring joy to a not-so-joyous body.

So before my next visit, I drew a lightning bolt and cloud on my breast with felt-tip markers. When he came into the examination room, I threw open my blouse to reveal my masterpiece. I had lost every bit of modesty with this man. He had already seen more of me than I could have ever imagined.

He was impressed. "Wow, if I had known you were an artist, I would have thought about doing this for you."

I was disappointed. I would have loved a pretty souvenir of my troubles.

My breasts looked great. Except for the large but subtle zipper across the top of my left breast, you could not tell the fake from the natural one. It had been a tough road, but the payoff was worth it.

Except for the depression, constant lethargy, and 4 P.M. headaches, I was back to normal and ready to get back to my life.

I was ready to get back to designing. After Kelley and Chelsea were born, I quit my full-time clothing design career to work from home part-time, developing limited lines of clothing I sold to such stores as Nordstrom (a Seattle-based national department store chain most locals knew as Nordie's), as well as to small boutiques and by word of mouth.

"It seems like your designs coincide with whatever phase the girls are in," Alan once joked. "Before they were born, you designed baby announcements. When they were born, you designed baby clothes, then outerwear for toddlers."

He was right. I decided to make a line of silk-screened shirts combined with crazy leggings for both girls and women. The more color and patterns the better. I created colorful illustrations to print on the sweatshirts and even went so far as to sew some of the garments myself. I hated sewing, but this was a cost-efficient way to go. I mixed and layered vibrant patterns on top of patterns. The outfits sold well.

I happily wore my own shirt designs, but I never had the nerve to wear the leggings. I was still most comfortable in jeans and sweats.

As the resident eccentric, I was still the neighborhood Bohemian. I was also the carpool queen and loving every minute of it. On some days, I would put 150 miles on the car while working on my ventures, or taking Kelley, Chelsea, and friends to their classes and activities.

In this way, our everyday suburban lives went on, but beneath the surface, I felt terrible. My 4 p.m. headaches would not go away, and I felt a dull pain and depression all the time. Some days I would get everyone off in the morning and head back to bed, sleeping as late as 1 P.M. I also had abdominal pain and worked with my family doctor to relieve that and the depression.

"Last year, all the meds I was taking began with a *P*," I observed at one visit.

My doctor cocked his head a bit, as if to say, hmm, had not noticed.

"Well, I guess this will be my *C* year," I quipped.

He looked at the list of medications we had decided I would try. "Guess you're right. I hope the *C* year helps."

CHAPTER NINE

Inside Out

I continued to struggle with the pain and depression. Acting as my own shrink, I decided it might be good therapy to take a sculpting class. I had not yet discovered that I had any sculpting abilities, although as a child I had carved turtles from bars of soap. As I mentioned before, going to classes is not something I usually stick with, but I was hopeful that I would follow through with this class. My creative voice was telling me to do this.

The studio was on the second floor of a two-story storefront in an older area of town. It felt artsy and quaint. The class was small, so the instructor could spend quality time with each student. We were allowed to work on any clay project we wanted, and most students wanted to learn how to use the potter's wheel. That was not for me. I wanted to sculpt.

Many designers tended to look down at fine artists, as everyone and their brother calls themselves as they seek their "passion." Getting paid to design gave a legitimacy to our work that most fine artists never achieve. At least it did in my mind. Working as a clothing designer, I'd dismissed many artists as self-indulgent.

If I was going to do fine art, I wanted my art to be edgy, very different from the cute designs I created for my clothing lines.

So I did. I sculpted a human head that turned out to be anything but cute. The terra cotta clay was rough and grainy.

44

The sculpture included the neck and shoulders, so it was technically a bust, and it stood about 10 inches tall. The face had a glazed look of despair, gazing into nowhere. The eyelids slumped over the protruding eyeballs, with nowhere to look. No pupils, no eyelashes, just a lifeless gaze. A minimal nose led to sparse lips which barely touched each other, and a breathy whisper seemed to be desperately trying to communicate.

Now, where in the world had that come from?

For the first time, my pain and emotion came out of me and spoke to the world. I was calm about the process, perplexed by the result, and uncertain about the message. The instructor had helped with the technique, but the head had created itself, with me just following its lead. That entire process was certainly a change from the controlled and preplanned designs of my past.

"That's a haunting head," the instructor remarked.

She was right. I had not paid much attention to it as I was creating it. I had just let it happen.

"Does it have any significant meaning to you, as to why you made it so haunting?"

I pressed my lips together and thought about that for a few seconds, trying to conjure up a story of love lost or something. "No," I finally said, evading the truth. "It's just what it is." But I knew. I knew that it represented the loss of part of me, both physically and mentally. Even with the relief of knowing I'd never again have cancer in that breast, it had been a long and painful ordeal I'd stoically and logically embraced, endured, and survived. Now I could release that emotion and hopefully move on.

"I'd love to buy it from you," she continued.

I was shocked that she thought it had any value, but I needed to keep it. It represented my private pain. I could not share that with anyone.

The head came home with me and hid behind knickknacks. Every once in a while, he would peer out from the corner, but I would never really look at him, just a glance before moving along. (I don't know why he was a *he*, but I'm sure that a shrink might like to get a hold of that one, especially because he looked like a *she*.) He haunted me. I hated him. I am surprised I never gave him away, as I did so many other objects I didn't need.

My new breast was beautiful, almost as perfect as the original. When I glanced into the mirror, sometimes I couldn't tell which was real and which was the fake. Sure, there was a scar on the top, but it drooped with just the right droop, just the right teardrop oval, and my areola looked real. I was feeling complete on the outside, yet lousy inside.

Physically and mentally, I hurt with every fiber of my body. The depression, aches, and pains were chronic. It was a chore to get out of bed, I just wanted to sleep and continually pop Excedrin and Pepcid. But I had come to terms with this dichotomy between my breasts and my health, and I lived with it.

When I had a job interview for a part-time freelance position as a clothing designer, I realized it was finally time to stretch my wardrobe beyond jeans and sweatshirts. My body looked good, and this was the perfect opportunity to expand my clothing comfort zone, so I decided to use a personal shopper at Nordstrom. I did not usually shop there, let alone use a personal shopper, but Nordie's seemed like the most likely place to find clothes that would say, "I'm a professional yet artsy woman—take me on!" Even a clothing designer needs a little help every once in a while.

Nordstrom was in an exclusive mall in Bellevue, the nouveau riche area of greater Seattle. The mall had been anchored long ago by Sears and JCPenney, and remnants of its modest origins were still there despite attempts to create a snobby, upscale image. Nordstrom was a special world. The familiar, comforting piano player was always there, playing happy tunes to stimulate our shopping experience. The smell of coffee wafted from the stylish coffee stand.

The personal shopper's office was in the corner behind the Givenchy and Chanel evening gowns. I was intimidated yet at home. Although I was not part of the couture fashion world, I knew it, understood it, and loved it.

"Is there a special event you'd like an outfit for?" the shopper asked. She was somewhere in her late thirties or early forties, and she seemed nonjudgmental. I was comfortable with her.

"I have a job interview as a clothing designer, and I need a professional but artistic outfit," I explained. She must have thought it odd that a clothing designer would need help with her own clothing, but I had designed menswear, children's wear, and outerwear, and at least I had the sense to know that most of my designs would look terrible on me.

"Let's get you going, and we'll knock their socks off," she said confidently. She seemed excited at the opportunity to take on this soccer mom/clothing designer wanna-be. I was an insecure little girl inside, asking mom to dress me, but I managed to put on a confident exterior. Just don't sweat, I told myself.

I followed her around the store like a puppy dog, agreeing to try on anything that she suggested. I hate trying on clothes, especially in front of others, but I closed my eyes, gritted my teeth, and embraced the experience. She leaned towards more classic looks than I would have thought. I envisioned that she would have picked out a complex strange combination that would scream artsy, but instead she picked out pencil skirts and blazers.

As I describe this outfit, please remember that it was the early nineties. She put together a plaid blazer, with shades of deep violet, yellow ochre, and black. Sounds hideous, but it was a subtle plaid, and the fit was perfect. She paired that with a black pencil skirt, black tee, black tights, and low black suede heels. The outfit screamed professional, yet a bit edgy. It was perfect.

A few days later, I met the owner of the clothing company at a downtown private club. He was impressed and flew me to his offices in San Francisco, where I met the other designer. It was a perfect opportunity. Only one problem. When I arrived at the offices, the designer was confused about why I was there. Turns out the owner had forgotten to tell her that he was thinking about adding another designer. She put the kibosh on that idea real fast.

That was the end of that, but now I had a new look, and I was ready to go on to the next design opportunity that presented itself. New book, new look, I'm on my way to being okay.

Then one morning, totally out of the blue, I woke up to find my new breast swollen. It felt as big as a watermelon. Still in bed, I dropped my chin down to look at my lopsided breasts. The newbie one looked unusually stretched, not red or anything else out of order. Out of the blue! Just one morning, with no warning, no reason, no nothing. As I sat up and looked down, I felt the pressure of gravity pulling on the breast. Not a good look. My hand cupped the breast. It spilled around my small hand, dwarfing my other breast.

Helloooooooo, Dolly Parton. I looked down and felt my breast. It was warm, but not hot, tender, but not hurting. I was perplexed, not yet scared.

I phoned Dr. Jacoby's office. "I look like Dolly Parton on my left side." My voice was calm, but inside I was a becoming a nervous wreck. I started playing with my hair. Gray was rearing its ugly head amid the dark brown; my gray strands felt kinkier than the others.

The nurse, who knew of my headaches, pain, and depression, went to talk to Dr. Jacoby, then came back on the line. "Can you come in ASAP?"

CHAPTER TEN

Farewell to Thee, Dolly Parton

D r. Jacoby looked at the nurse then back at me. "Let's see what we can do with antibiotics and bed rest, but I'm worried. If the swelling doesn't go down in five days, we will have to remove the implant."

That was not going to happen. I had worked too hard, and it looked too good. Unfortunately, my breast did not agree, and five days later, in Dr. Jacoby's office operating room, my breast and I would part ways.

Brenda drove me to and from Dr. Jacoby's outpatient clinic because I had not been able to get hold of Alan. My nerves shattered, I wanted him there, but knew that I could do this on my own. It actually helped me stay strong that he wasn't there to worry. Of course I resented his work for making him unreachable, but dwelling on that would not help my current situation. Just do it, just get this over with, just move on, you have no choice. Damn it.

By now I was used to every corner of my doctor's office. The lobby was warm and cozy, the doctor's office also warm and cozy. Not so much the "work room." It felt larger than an examination room, but smaller than a surgery room (I felt like I had become an expert on procedure rooms). It was cold. Cold blue walls, cold blue furniture, cold blue doctor's robes, just like a scene out of the movie *Frozen*.

The clank of surgical instruments echoed in the barren

room. My examination table was centered in the room with all sorts of equipment surrounding me. I disrobed just on the top, donned the all-familiar surgical attire and laid down on the table. I need to design a better pattern for these robes, I thought.

I was not happy. I was not a quitter and I had given so much to make this breast work. Stay stoic, I told myself. At least I won't have to worry about all of the reports of ruptured implants and consequences of having a prosthetic. My life had always had choices, but this one was not mine to control. Stay stoic.

The doctor gave me a mild sedative, so I was awake the entire time. He removed the implant with no trouble, and luckily, it had not leaked. I started to feel pain and discomfort as he scraped the remaining breast tissue away from my chest. I could feel the pressure of the scalpel and hear the scraping, like fingernails across a chalkboard. I felt sick and defeated. He was taking away what I had endured so much to keep. It seemed to take forever. All I could think about was how defeated and alone I felt.

My instructions were to go home and rest. There was nothing more to do.

As a footnote, after my mastectomy the FDA came out with a warning about the type of implant I had. It was apparently so problematic that it was then taken off the market. Unfortunately, a similar implant is now on the market.

As we drove home, my body was, as usual, not happy with the anesthesia.

"I need a Pepsi," I insisted to Brenda. "Could we please stop and get a Pepsi?" I thought it would help settle my stomach.

It didn't. Sorry, Brenda. I'll get the car cleaned.

"Pull over, quick" became a repeated request and the three-mile drive home turned into a marathon. In between stops, I cried.

It was no doubt a ridiculous scene to anyone following

behind. This brand new monster of an SUV stopping and starting on small residential roads while what appeared to be a soccer mom repeatedly leaned out of the car to throw up.

Lots of new families had moved into the neighborhood in the eighteen months since my diagnosis, and Brenda and I had planned a neighbor get-together at the community center for this evening. We had made maps of the neighborhood with names of the residents. Decorations, refreshments and party activities had all been meticulously planned. We were all looking forward to meeting each other.

"I'm not going to be able to help you with the party tonight."

"Well, duh," she laughed, trying to bring some levity to the situation. I appreciated that.

I insisted that Alan, Kelley, and Chelsea attend the neighborhood party.

I wanted to be alone.

CHAPTER ELEVEN

Life Lopsided

My perfectly reconstructed breast was gone. I had been defeated, which I never took well. I was stubborn and compulsive, yet my fight to keep my breast had come to an end. Losing a breast was hardly the worst thing that could ever happen, I tried to tell myself.

Until this moment, I had not allowed myself self-pity, but now I was feeling pretty sorry for myself. Even the zipper on the top of my breast was starting to show the wear and tear of being used way too much.

On the bright side, the 4 p.m. headaches were not as constant. I had more energy. It was gradual, but I was feeling better. Physiologically better, anyway. But lopsided. Not only that, I had an ugly mass of loose skin where once there had been a beautiful breast. The skin that had been stretched for the implant was saggy and deflated. Ripples of skin lay across my chest, joined by a fatty mass that ended under my arm, where the bulb for the pumping-up sessions had been.

Why hadn't my beloved Dr. Jacoby cleaned up the mess when he removed the implant? Perhaps he thought that I might reconsider trying again with an implant, but for now, it was just plain ugly and messy.

Why hadn't I gone back to him to have him clean it up? Easy, I just wanted to move on. I couldn't imagine having any more surgery, no matter how small.

Frankly, the loss of my hard-fought breast outweighed any thought of the carnage that was left. I didn't reconsider another implant.

The HMO ordered a prosthesis for me. It did not matter to them if I had a breast or not, or that I had made such a valiant effort to keep the breast they had paid for. It was all routine for them.

They referred me to a specialty store near the Nordstrom mall in Bellevue, in an area that was still being transformed into the new upscale image. Twenty-story glass-walled office buildings and condominiums were rising into the sky with such rapidity that every day a new obstruction seemed to appear along the horizon.

The makeover had forgotten this store. Tucked between the uber-contemporary multiuse buildings, amid the cranes creating the new face of Bellevue, sat this small one-story, single-store building, painted off-white with blue trim. It had its own parking lot, rarely found these days among the giant parking garages of the busy downtown area. With its cedar roof and double Dutch doors, it might have been someone's house long ago.

A small sign hung above the doors. You could easily miss it, which I guess was the point—to be discreet about such subjects as missing boobs in this town of beautiful people.

Close your eyes, grit your teeth, and do it.

Taking a deep breath, I opened the small white double Dutch door to my new life. I thought I might find camaraderie and comfort, inside, but no, I had walked straight into the fifties and was greeted by a relic of the same era.

"Hello, how are you?" She was old. All the employees were old. They wore too much makeup, as if they were hoping the layers of foundation would cover the years of wrinkles, but the makeup only made the wrinkles more prominent. The hairstyles were frozen in time and in place—coiffed, set, and sprayed to death, never to move again. Their hair looked freshly dyed in my least-favorite red/brown noncolor, but I did catch glimpses of gray at the roots, indicating it was time for a beauty parlor appointment. I wish the hair dye companies would come up with a better "old lady" color. Maybe purple.

Their outfits were just that—outfits, ensembles. Not a casually chosen blouse and a skirt, but put-together, purposeful outfits, which did not mean their choices were great. Polyester suits, with polyester ruffled blouses peeking from the jacket. The colors of their clothes were artificial, just like the breast prostheses they sold—baby blue, a pink that should not exist.

The entire building and its contents were artificial.

"My HMO sent me here to get fitted for a breast prosthesis," I said calmly, trying to keep any emotion from showing.

"Well, dear, you are in the right place."

Here we go again with the honeys, sweeties, and dears.

With the same pitying look that a nurse gives you when she knows that you are in pain, she gestured for me to go into the dressing room and undress. I suppose that she was trying to be compassionate, but I found it condescending. The other saleswomen were rigid and cold, looking away from me as if I did not exist. I served no purpose to them; the commission was spoken for by the lady now trying to help me.

I had not been this uncomfortable in . . . ever. I was about to undress and expose my lopsided, scar-ridden chest. I undressed and waited. I had not worn a bra because my remaining breast was small enough to get away without one, and of course I had my baggiest clothes on. I was in my overalls phase and looked like a hillbilly, which did nothing to impress the sales staff. I was one of those pathetic clueless clients contractually sent to them by the bourgeois HMO.

It seemed an eternity.

"You're a A/B cup. Right?" She took out a measuring tape and wrapped it around my chest. The tape drooped unceremoniously into the gap of my missing breast. "We can fit you into an A/B cup, or we can increase the cup size and provide you with an insert for the other side so you can be larger . . . and look so much better."

She was checking out my chest while trying to assess and re-create me. Never had I been more exposed.

"No, thank you," I mumbled timidly as I covered my chest. "I think I'll stay an A/B cup."

"Whatever you say." Her disapproval showing, she turned quickly to get the prosthesis.

"Here you go." She thrust a box at me. A heavy pink twelve-by-twelve-inch box with a photo of a woman's face on it, also straight out of the fifties—blue eyes, classic red lipstick, and perfectly styled blonde hair. Her head was tilted slightly, with one manicured hand delicately cupping her chin. She was blissfully at peace. "A Woman's Happy Experience" was written in a soft white that contrasted gently with the pink of the box. A hinge at one end opened to expose the neatly packed silicone breast lying on top of a plastic form, which cupped its treasure perfectly. The cardboard was much heavier than that of most boxes today. They had spent a lot of money on that packaging.

Who were they kidding? This was a cold, plastic excuse for a woman's missing body part.

I gently lifted the prosthesis from its nest and was surprised by how heavy it was.

"It's anatomically correct in every way," the saleslady proudly pointed out.

My replacement breast was sort of an almond shape and had defined sides. The side that went around toward the underarm was elongated to mimic the muscle that wraps around the chest. The top tapered out to give a nice line toward the décolleté area, and the bottom had Dr. Jacoby's precious proper droop.

"It's heavy," I smirked, trying to interject a bit of lightness into this stodgy old lady.

"These are made to be perfectly correct in every way, even

to the correct weight of your breast," she haughtily explained.

Oh joy. The least they could have done was make the stupid thing lighter so we could weigh less than we did when we had breasts.

The prosthesis comes with triangular pieces of Velcro, about the same size as your breast area. First, you remove the protective paper from the sticky side and mash it against your chest, positioning it where you hope the breast will look most natural. Then, you take the breast out of its very special box and smash the Velcroed side of that against the Velcro fabric attached to your chest. Instant breast.

But the weight of the prosthesis pulls the skin away from your body, even with a size A/B, so a bra, which I *hate* wearing, is mandatory. And even then, your bra is not quite anchored under the breast since the breasts are not that well attached to your body, so slight migration ensues. Nothing is in place, but nothing is out of place, and everything is uncomfortable.

Supposedly, the triangular fabric can stay on your body for up to five days, even when showering and sleeping. But if you try this, it feels like a constricting super-sized Band-Aid across your chest, pulling at you as you move. And if you wear it in the shower, it feels like a wet clam and starts to unstick, even if you had just put it on that day.

I tried to wear the prosthesis without the Velcro, but I was always scared that this synthetic creature would pop out of my bra or get a mind of its own and move to a place where it felt more comfortable. This was my future. The prosthesis was expensive and uncomfortable, but I told myself that in time, I would learn to love my new buddy.

The discomfort did not outweigh the benefits. I knew summers would be especially hard, as my chest sweated beneath the unbreathing bag of silicone. I wore the prosthesis as little as possible and turned to my baggy clothes to hide my lopsidedness.

What surprised me most was how much I hated knowing that I was lopsided.

On one side was the well-worn zipper, which had been opened three times with nothing to show for it, just saggy skin and a fading tattoo. I dreaded taking showers; I hated looking at my lopsided body. I hated showering, washing my chest and toweling off, and I especially hated looking in the mirror. It was a constant reminder of what I had fought so hard to keep and had lost anyway.

The stress was taking its toll.

"Alan, *damn it*, clean up your climbing equipment. You've been home from your trip for weeks now, and your stuff is still spread all over the room."

"Kelley, for god's sake, put the books back when you're done reading."

"Chelsea, when in the world are you going to practice your trumpet?"

"Slow down," Alan would sit me down on our bed, still perfectly decorated, away from the kids.

"You have a breast exam this week, don't you. Your stress level is through the roof and you're taking it out on us."

He was right. It had only been six months since I lost my implant, but two years since the whole ordeal started. There wasn't a day that went by that I didn't worry about the next suspicious lump. Just like it seems like everyone is pregnant when you're pregnant, it seemed that breast cancer was in every corner of my life. Friends talking about it, articles in the news, the fear of little breast cancer cells growing in my remaining breast. It was a fluke that they found the original cancer; now I was beyond scared that cancer was developing in my other breast and I would have no clue until it was too late.

I was getting mammograms every month, and every month I went through the same thing.

"There is a small cloudy area on the latest mammogram. Let's do an ultra sound and check it out."

It seemed like my car drove on autopilot as it knew the route to the doctor's office so well.

I couldn't take the roller coaster any more. I had to take action.

My beloved Dr. Williams understood. We decided it was time to take the other breast. With my history and new lumps, it made sense. A drastic move, yes, but we all agreed it was the right thing to do. My mental health was as important as my physical health.

With my history of having surgeries to celebrate holidays, this was my Valentine's Day present. Oh boy, a new zipper! I was hoping he would put this one below my breast.

Here I was again, lying in the operating room, waiting to be put to sleep, questioning what in the world I was doing, by choice, no less. Knowing my usual reaction to surgery, I wondered if this was the dumbest move I had ever made. What would happen if something went wrong and I died? My children were young; they needed their mom. This was really stupid. I was more scared than I had ever been.

This was not necessary. Yet I knew it was.

"How're you doing, honey?" the nurse asked as she gently touched my thigh.

We had seen each other so often that I guess we were finally close enough to use those endearing names.

The doctors and I knew the routine. It was over; I had no more breast to give. With my history, Dr. Jacoby refused to consider the possibility of using implants. He was right. I was devastated.

The pain after surgery was terrible. I had just been through multiple surgeries in a short amount of time, so I plugged on. This was not going to bother me; it was just a stumbling block. But the pain became so intolerable that I called the doctor—and to my horror, he wanted me to remove the extra drain myself. *Really?* I can do this? REALLY?

The drain was located under my arm in the flabby area to the side of where a breast used to be. The plastic tubing stuck out from my skin, coiled around for about 18 inches, and was attached to a plastic bag collecting the yellowish reddish goo coming from the body. Gross.

"All you have to do is grab onto the tubing where it enters your body and gently pull it out."

Simple! Really?! You've got to be kidding.

"You can do it. It will make you much more comfortable."

I was desperate. I stood by the side of my bed, tears running down my face, alone in my big house. I closed my eyes and pulled. I felt a tug around the skin area but nothing inside of me. I was sickened by images of a plastic tube dragging inside of me as I tugged, but I kept gently pulling. Within a few seconds, which seemed like hours, the end of the tube appeared. There was a release of pressure around the incision and I took a huge breath. I had been standing this entire time next to the small bucket by the bed where I kept the drainage bag. The tube and bag drooped unceremoniously into the bucket and I dropped equally unceremoniously onto the bed, sitting on the side of the bed with my head between my legs to prevent myself from passing out or throwing up.

I did it!

I am invincible, I can do anything.

I am very flat.

CHAPTER TWELVE

The Rise of Annie Flats

Back to the prosthesis store and my favorite ladies. I decided to stay with my natural cup size, A/B.

"Very well," Miss Prissy muttered. "Your choice."

I could hear them thinking, *why in the world would she do that?* This was my opportunity to be any size I wanted. Why would I not want to be as big as possible? But I liked being small. From my hippie, braless days in New York, it was my statement of comfort and nonconformity. As much as I kept trying to fit into my surroundings, my inner core was one of nonconformity and individuality.

I was an active person. I chopped wood in my yard and built structures for my kids to play on. Large breasts would just get in my way. My breast size was the only small thing about me. With little fanfare, I received another pink cardboard box, a second anatomically correct and accurately weighted breast, and a bag of Velcro stick-ems.

I continued to wear overalls, sweatshirts, and baggy tees, and I began to question whether you could tell I had breasts at all. The prostheses spent more time in their boxes. I told myself I was saving money by not having to buy the expensive Velcro strips.

In an organic progression, I stopped having breasts. I was mainly home doing active homeworking jobs wearing baggy, formless clothes. Sure, I wondered what I looked like to others, but at this point, I didn't care. I didn't feel feminine, but I didn't feel exactly non-feminine.

But—I did feel liberated. I did not have to wear a bra! Unless they are very large-chested, most women take off their bras as soon as they get home. I did not even have to put one on! Being flat became a personal statement; I could still be a woman even if I did not have breasts. Gloria Steinman would have been proud. This was my fashion statement. So, here we go:

The Good: The comfort, omg, *the comfort!* No restrictive uncomfortable bra, no bra straps falling off the shoulder or showing in the wrong places, and oh yes, the expense. I could save money by not buying bras!

No more mammograms! There was no breast to check. No plastering my breast onto the cold plexiglass shelf.

The scare of breast cancer was gone. Done. Game over.

Camisoles. I tended to wear a camisole under whatever I was wearing and it was soooooo comfortable. Plain camisoles, lacy camisoles, sporty camisoles. The sky was the limit.

Dance class. I would throw a baggy tee over a leotard, and off I would go. I wasn't ready to reveal my deformed body to anyone, so the baggy clothes were perfect. I could jump, run, twist—do anything I wanted—and not have breasts flopping around like the other women in the class. I stayed cooler too.

The Bad: I was self-conscious about hugs. Do people expect to feel a bra when putting their arms around a woman? The back strap of a bra was almost always visible or at least one would feel it when being hugged. That roll of skin seems to be the bane of many a woman. I wondered if they were surprised not to feel one. Did people wonder where the breasts were when they hugged me? Breasts act as a cushion between people. My boundaries were gone. A hug became more of a smash. As I hugged someone I wondered what their thoughts were when surprised with a smash rather than a squish.

And the Ugly: My chest is gross. The skin that was stretched to hold an implant is now a rippled mess of saggy scar tissue and skin, definitely an improper droop. In addition, the faded tattooed nipple is still there, but way too low. On the other side, where I had the latest mastectomy, the skin is fairly flat and smooth, almost concave. Dr. Williams was considerate enough to put the scar on the bottom of my chest. Thank you, Dr. Williams, but I wish the other side had been cleaned up, too. I was so focused on the mastectomy that it never occurred to me to ask.

But I moved on and started experimenting with the color of my now-graying hair. It started out innocently enough, but I think Kelley and Chelsea eventually started a betting pool: "What color will Mom's hair be today?"

"Mom, you need a dye job," was Chelsea's friendly reminder to keep the pool active.

I went from dark brown, my natural color, to streaks of blonde, to quite blonde, and on to the ever-so-popular and memorable red phase. Not a natural red, as I had wanted, but a bright pinky red.

One week, the gray was slowly overtaking whatever color I had last used, so I decided to go platinum. Short, spiky platinum hair with huge overalls.

Nice image, soccer mom.

Life returned to our "normal"—a revolving door of activities and people. I purchased a huge Chevy Suburban SUV. (I know, I know, we were *not* going to be one of those suburban, materialistic, gas-guzzling families, but the purchase would be justified later.) We could fit lots and lots of kids into it, so I returned to being carpool mom, complete with my open bag of coffee at my side.

Fall was soccer season for Chelsea, one of the many sports involving balls that she loved. We went to all the games, many of them early in the morning. Seattle is definitely not the driest place on earth, so the soccer fields were often covered in a dense fog, which usually burned off around halftime. The moms came up with creative outfits to deal with the cold, wet weather.

"Love the neon one-piece suit you found," a mom would comment.

"Where did you find the deep-sea fishing suit? I simply must have one," another would squeal.

We layered the outerwear over long underwear and polar fleece. As the fog dissipated, we would shed each layer until, by the end of the game, we were left wearing clothing that was actually appropriate for being in public. For me, the more layers the better. My overalls and sweats were perfect.

In keeping with Alan's observation regarding my clothing designs coinciding with my state of motherhood, mainly the kids' never-ending sporting events, my friend Mary and I decided to start a line of promotional garments for sporting events. We would customize sweatshirts, T-shirts, and other items with an event's logo and then sell the items at the games. I created unusual and very colorful logos which distinguished us from other companies.

We bought a machine to press the designs onto the garments and purchased massive amounts of sweats, tees, and hats. But we still had not agreed on a name for the company.

It was during one of our walks that the perfect name hit me.

"I know this name is crazy," I blurted, "but what do you think of Annie Flats? It's a wide spot in the road in central northwestern Washington State, named after Alan's grandmother, who was a huge part of his life. She was the postmistress on the Indian reservation where Alan grew up. It's just a funny name. You can be Annie, and I can be Flats. After all, I *am* flat."

"I love it!"

The sun peaked out from the morning fog, and Annie Flats was born. Our company grew quickly. I handled the creative and manufacturing end, and Mary handled the business end. We packed the clothes into my Suburban (see, this is why I needed the Suburban), and off we went. As I was usually the person booking the job, people assumed that my name was

Annie Flats, and lo and behold, Annie and Ms. Flats were born. Really. Everyone thought my last name was Flats. I liked the name Annie, so I went with it. It stuck around for a long time, but eventually, I returned to just being Lynne. It was just too much work and confusion to be two different people.

Soon it became clear that our friendship was more important than our partnership, so we decided that I would buy Mary out and venture forward on my own.

In this new partnership, I was Annie, and my chest was Flats.

CHAPTER THIRTEEN

Strength in Numbers

Over the next few years, Alan and I amassed a collection of cars: the Suburban, a smaller SUV which was getting up in mileage, an old Camry, and a convertible VW named Ollie. It was a car menagerie. We saw our local mechanics so much, I affectionately referred to them as "my guys." The environmentally conscious hippies of the Pacific Northwest we had once imagined ourselves to be had succumbed. Here we were, with four cars (one of them enormous), living in a huge house in the land of Microsoft multimillionaires.

We also had a menagerie of pets, from our dog Beans to Kelley's grumpy cat, Suki. We had an unintentional habit of naming our pets after food.

Kelley was an avid ice skater, and I loved watching her practice at the ice rink partly because I could bundle up in clothes. I tried to stay away from the skating moms as best I could. One exception was Gail, who had moved from Los Angeles with her daughter, a talented skater who had been paired with a boy from Seattle. It was common for a girl to move to where her partner lived. Since there were many more girls than boys in the skating world, the boy usually dictated the location—just one more part of the skating world that I wanted my daughter to avoid. Gail and I became close friends during the six months she and her daughter were in Seattle. They moved to Sun Valley, Idaho, and eventually Kentucky, and in the years to come, I would visit her often. Her Sun

Valley home became my special getaway place.

Kelley's skating coach attracted skaters from all over the globe. The visiting skaters and their parents needed places to stay, so we offered to house them and ended up with yet another menagerie—of people. Alan described our house as a revolving door and renamed it the Hanson Hotel. I figured it would be fun to get to know skaters from around the world, and it would be good for Kelley and Chelsea to learn about different cultures. Maybe this is where Chelsea developed the wanderlust that later led her all over the globe.

Our entourage of skaters came from England, Japan, Canada, Australia, and various places in the States. At one point, we had six skaters from Australia with some of their parents. Between my girls, their friends from school, and the skaters, we literally had people sleeping in our hallways. Hotel Hanson was in full force, and I was in heaven. I drove the entire lot of kids to skating, basketball, soccer, music lessons, and school. I made large batches of pancakes and waffles for breakfast, and my baked ziti became a staple for dinner. Alan taught the kids how to fly fish.

Trent, an Australian skater, became obsessed with all our gardening equipment. Because we had a full acre of manicured lawn, we had a riding lawn mower, which Trent loved to take apart and put back together after he finished mowing. We also had a branch chipper, which Trent called our "chippah."

"I'm headed out to work on the chippah," he would cheerfully announce.

"Have fun and be careful," I'd yell as he headed outdoors.

"No worries," was always his answer. Loved that: No worries.

I was thrilled because the yard work was mainly my job, and I hated it. Trent adopted us as his U.S. family, called me Mum, and returned many times to stay with us as he trained. His mother visited often as well, and we instantly bonded. They became a part of our family.

Another skater, Ty, also became part of our family. He started training at the rink when he was twelve, and at fourteen, he went through a growth spurt, surpassing even Kelley in height. Around that time, he began living with us. It worked well because he was about the same age as Kelley and Chelsea, and they were able to attend the same schools.

Thin and graceful, Ty moved like a dancer even when doing the most ordinary things. On one of his first mornings with us, Alan came into the kitchen to find the counter transformed into a ballet barre, where Ty was dutifully doing his stretches. Though Alan was not used to seeing men, or anyone else for that matter, doing ballet on his kitchen counter, stretching at the kitchen ballet barre became a morning ritual for the two of them. They grew very close.

Ty's mother was also dealing with breast cancer when we met, so Ty and my family bonded over cancer as well as ice-skating. Unfortunately, Ty was only sixteen when she passed away.

CHAPTER FOURTEEN

Mona Soup and Matzo Ball Soup

In the fall of Kelley's sophomore year in high school, she began to sleep more and more and was not able to keep any food inside her.

"I need to come home. I don't feel well." The phone calls from school became more and more frequent.

Eating disorders and depression were rampant in the sport of skating, so I assumed that the pressure of having the perfect tiny skating body had gotten to her as it had to so many. I had bucked society's values regarding breasts and I was not going to let my daughter succumb to those pressures.

So it came as a shock when the psychologist and our family doctor informed me that she was fighting some sort of physical infection, but they couldn't find the cause. She just got weaker and weaker. During her junior year, her five-foot-seven frame was down to ninety-eight pounds, and she attended school only twenty-nine days. Kelley was prone to dark circles under her eyes due to her allergies, but her normally alabaster skin was now chalky, which only accentuated the circles around her almond eyes.

We were all at our wit's end.

Each of us handled it in our own way. Alan's way was denial. Chelsea tried to escape into school and her activities. I rearranged furniture.

When Alan would come home late, which was often, he would trip over furniture that had not been in that spot when he had left earlier that day. He quickly learned to turn on the lights before entering a room.

I closed my business to stay home with Kelley. I made sure to keep a batch of Annie Flats' baggy sweats and tees for the two of us. Kelley and I would pile on the layers, her to stay warm and me to hide.

I became an expert at making matzo ball soup, the all-purpose Jewish penicillin, though it turned out the soup was more for me than for her. To this day, Kelley hates matzo ball soup.

I thought a kitten might bring some laughter into our home, so Kelley and I went to see what was supposed to be a blue point Siamese kitten. I had always wanted one. The breeder greeted us in a long, flowery dress, like a true relic from the flower child generation. We followed her into the living room, where three kittens were playing.

"Here they are." She motioned for us to sit on the floor if we wanted to see them.

Two were red point Siamese. The third was a beautiful striped grayish brown, but definitely not a blue point.

I wasn't happy. "I was under impression that you had a blue point."

"She is a blue point," the lady insisted.

I don't know what drugs this lady was on, but judging from the bongs around the room, I could guess.

I wasn't going to argue with her, so I picked up the tiny kitten. *No wonder this lady can't see what color she is,* I thought. The poor kitten had almost no hair. Her belly was distended, and her right foot was clubbed, bent from the ankle joint inward. She had six toes on three of her feet, including on the clubfoot.

The kitten was a sorry sight. To make matters worse, the lady proudly pointed out the old-fashioned pop-bead necklaces she'd put on the kittens to get them used to wearing collars. She had forgotten to add beads as they grew and it was digging into the pathetic kitty's neck. Kelley and I looked at each other in amazement. This lady was supposed to be a reputable, responsible breeder. She was anything but.

"That one is $150. Isn't she cute?"

She was endearing, for sure. This tiny, pathetic, club-footed, hairless creature wasn't what we'd come to see, but she needed us, and we needed her.

"I can't pay that for a kitten with a club foot," was my starting point. I was trying not to yell, "This kitten is a mess, you irresponsible woman! Just let me rescue her!"

"I'll take $80."

"She'll need to go to the vet, and I don't know how much it'll cost. We'll give her a great home."

I don't think the offer of a great home did any good, but the thought of vet bills probably did. She finally agreed to give her to us. Kelley ripped off the pop beads as we left.

We named her Mona Soup, a stage name Kelley had made up for herself when one of her friends was shooting a film. There's a film out there with Mona Soup in the credits.

The next day I took her to the vet. "It was very nice of you to take the cat in," she said gently. "But her club foot is inoperable, and she'll live only a few weeks. At least you'll have her and she'll have you for that time."

I was devastated. This was unacceptable. I would take her home, and we would love her and make her well. Within two weeks, little Mona Soup was growing hair, and the distended belly was giving way to a healthy, full belly. Her clubbed foot straightened out by itself within just a few weeks. It was a sign. She was going to be okay.

Through all of the concern and work that it took to help Kelley and Mona, my health was on the back burner. As it'd been when Kelley was younger and had such severe allergic reactions we had to rush her to the emergency room, I would remain strong and stoic during the crisis. Then, when I knew she'd be okay, I would collapse. I had no time to deal with my issues or health and just plugged through whatever headaches, depression or other issues I had.

With my business shut down, I was going stir crazy. I wanted to stay home and throw myself into something new. I was exhausted but restless. I remembered my positive experience sculpting the clay head, and became intrigued with discovering more about myself as I explored the fine arts. Sacrilege, I know, to go into the realm of fine arts, but it was calling me.

I needed to be home all the time. *Learn to paint,* a little voice in the deep recesses of my brain told me. Well, painting *was* something that I could do at home. As I researched, I was drawn to what many considered the hardest subject— children—and the medium of oils. Perhaps the tactile aspects of oil painting was the draw. Painting children in oils was a challenge that would really push me. I liked challenges. If I could do that, I would consider myself a painter.

I did not want to leave the house to take classes. My parents had always taught us to just go out and do it, so that is what I did. I was sure I could teach myself. I read every book and magazine on painting I could get my hands on.

Painting soon filled every minute and I enjoyed every second. The work was filled with color. I warped color and pushed the limits of realism. Unexpected purples and blues would clash with lime greens in a portrait of a young girl. I was prolific, but now I needed homes for all these children I had painted.

An article about a young girl with an incurable disease caught my attention. Friends of the girl's family were organizing an auction to cover her medical expenses. I offered a painting for the auction. Then I found other worthwhile organizations and donated works to them, too. Both creating the paintings and the act of donating them took me out of my own worries and myopic world.

To my amazement and pleasure, people who attended

the fundraisers started calling to see if they could buy one of my paintings. Never one to turn down the opportunity to make money, I launched a new career. My world expanded to attending art fairs, and I got my work into a few small galleries.

My art and daughters were my jobs. I was part-time Lynne, part-time Annie, part-time mother, and part-time artist. Some of the time, I would use Annie as my name, and sometimes I would be Lynne. Some of the time I would dress with my flat chest proudly displayed, and sometimes I would hide in the baggiest outfit I could find. No one, not even me, knew who I was.

With the help of a very creative and helpful school counselor, Kelley was able to graduate with her classmates. She chose to go to college on the east coast, as she wanted a new experience, and she was able to find a small college in Maine which worked with her and her weakened immune system. We were all scared to have her 3,000 miles from home and her doctors, but the school was compassionate and helpful, and my extended family was close by in New York. A year later when Chelsea chose a college in Connecticut, I felt even more reassured.

With her safe at school, I was able to devote much more time to painting, and the paintings continued to sell.

"Have you painted today?" Alan's fingers would wrap around the door opening and he'd peek in, sensing whether it was safe to come into the room. He could tell when I hadn't been painting, because I'd be, as he put it, "impossibly grumpy."

Too true.

We spent hours together in our family room, which I'd transformed from a meticulously decorated gathering space to a multifunctional room, with me painting away at my super-sized easel while Alan sat at his brand new fly-tying desk, concentrating on the latest technique.

"Your paintings are beautiful, but it's time to push yourself and find your own style," he commented one evening.

"I know. I've been feeling that way for a while, but I'm surprised you noticed. I didn't think you paid attention."

I put on my new olive-green wingtip glasses.

Alan put on his coke-bottle-thick frameless glasses.

We went back to our obsessions.

My opportunity to refine my unique style came on a birthday when I was given the use of a condo in Sun Valley for one month. With my Suburban fully loaded, I set off with Beans and my bike for a month of self-exploration. I was spending less time as Annie and more time as Lynne. My paintings became more abstract, and more colorful. I switched my subject matter to horses and women in evening gowns. Funny how all the women were flat chested.

The house had emptied out. Kelley was in Maine, Chelsea in Connecticut, and Ty moved to New York City to skate with the prestigious Ice Theatre of New York.

Life moved on.

CHAPTER FIFTEEN

The 9/11 Snowball

You wouldn't think the tragedy of 9/11 would affect Seattle, but it hit hard. Just one of Seattle's employers laid off over thirty thousand people. The ripple effect hit us, and Alan too was laid off. We had two girls in private colleges, a large mortgage, me with minimal income potential, and Alan, middle-aged in corporate America—too experienced for some jobs, and too old for others.

"Maybe it's time for a drastic change." I was pacing across the family room, wrapping and unwrapping a strand of my now very gray hair around my finger, looking at the spreading bald spot on the back of Alan's head. He listened as his gaze followed the graceful line of his fly-fishing pole.

"If we're going to be unemployed somewhere," I continued, "it might as well be in a place that we love. We've always hoped that someday we would move back to a ski town." As newlyweds, we briefly lived in Telluride in 1973, but the oil embargo and a terrible drought had made it impossible to make a living there. We'd always planned on returning to that shared dream, to living the simple life of ski bums in a small town. Instead we'd taken a not-so-simple path up the West Coast to raise a family in the Pacific Northwest.

When we lived in Telluride, I was inspired to become a clothing designer. Skiwear was a color-filled painting on a beautiful backdrop of white snow and it drew me in. The colorful skiwear designs solidified my interest in how clothing,

74

color and texture affects the feminine body. I loved the color blocking that was popular at the time.

On a lark, I entered a contest to design "the perfect pair of pants" for Levi Strauss. Lo and behold, I placed third and won a Levi Strauss buckle belt! Oh boy! Even though I never wore the belt, the contest sparked my interest in clothing design.

I was living in a ski town at the top of the Rockies that was as isolated as you could get, wearing flannel shirts and jeans while perusing the latest high fashion magazines. Honestly, I never felt sexier than when I was back there wearing flannel shirts, jeans and skiwear. Perhaps I could regain that feeling.

I stopped pacing and stood in front of him until he looked up from his fishing pole. "Maybe this is our time."

Alan's eyes teared up.

We narrowed our choices down to Ashland, Oregon, or Bozeman, Montana. Bozeman had been our first choice as newlyweds, twenty-seven years ago. In fact, Alan's father's Norwegian family was originally from Montana. We weren't able to find jobs there, which was the only reason we didn't move to Bozeman then.

Maybe now *was* our time. Alan's cousin Lee lived in Bozeman and we visited a few times to scope out job and housing prospects with his help.

Then we put the house on the market.

"You need to paint your living room beige," the Realtor dictated. "The periwinkle will be a deterrent to selling the house."

My house was not beige and never would be beige. By now I had accepted who I was. My life, my body, and even my house would never conform, not even to sell the house during this terrible time.

We sold our house in one day, to a wonderful Iranian family. The extended family came to look at the house together, and when the grandfather, a little man, gingerly stepped into the living room, he looked around, sighed, and with a wide smile said softly, "Blue. It's *blue*."

You would think that this would have been a tough time, but for me, it was liberating. I donated or sold almost every piece of furniture we had, and we went from a full house to thirteen pieces of furniture, including beds. Luckily, Kelley and Chelsea were 3,000 miles away at school, so they didn't have to see their entire pasts flying out the front door.

"How are you doing, dear?" the neighbors asked sadly.

With a grin from ear to ear, I responded, "Great! I'm having the time of my life getting rid of all this stuff. We've sold all but two of our cars" (yes, I sold the Suburban), "we've furnished a home for a nonprofit organization, and we've either sold or given away just about everything we own. It feels *great.*"

I meant it.

Yes, I felt a twinge or two about leaving the house that I loved and had raised my family in, but I was more than ready for a new adventure. Sure, we'd also be leaving all the doctors we had formed close relationships with (at least in my mind, as I was still in love with my doctors). But I was doing well and so was Kelley, so I calculated the move was worth the risk. Worst-case scenario, they were available by phone.

This was one of the most liberating times for me in my healing process. The ugly clay head I had sculpted after my first mastectomy finally appeared from where it had been hiding. I knew it was time to purge whatever the head stood for. I took it to the backyard and smashed it into the rocks. Surprisingly fragile, it shattered into tiny pieces.

I walked away, not feeling a thing.

We negotiated to stay in the house through the end of the year so we could have one last family holiday there. Kelley and Chelsea came home to say good-bye to their friends, the house, and Seattle.

We had to be out of the house by January 5. On December 24 we had not yet decided where to live.

On December 26, I announced to the girls, "We're moving

to Bozeman. It makes the most sense. We know it better than Ashland and love it. Are you guys okay with that?"

It was a statement and a question that I did not want an honest answer to. Of course they wouldn't want to move. This was their home.

"We're with you guys." Kelley and Chelsea did not even look to see if the other agreed. "We support anything you decide to do."

I love my children.

CHAPTER SIXTEEN

Moving On

January 4.

We put Chelsea on a plane for her semester abroad in Prague.

With the help of Kelley's friends, we loaded all our possessions into a seventeen-foot-long U-Haul truck.

That night, Kelley, Alan, and I slept in our empty 4,500-square-foot home on a couple of mattresses we were giving to friends. We were lost in our own thoughts. I hoped that Kelley was thinking about her upcoming semester in Paris rather than leaving her Seattle past behind.

January 5.

Alan, Kelley, and I took off on the 750-mile drive to Bozeman with our dog, two cats, two cars, and a truck. Alan drove the U-Haul in the lead; Kelley followed him in the old SUV; and I brought up the rear in our Camry. I was entertained by watching the cats' heads popping up and down in Kelley's rear window.

I was happy for Alan, as we were off to the land of his ancestors and he would have nature at his footsteps. He felt very close to his heritage; communing with nature was in his DNA. At a rest stop, I kidded him, "You're coming full circle, going upstream to where you began. You're just like a salmon."

Oh, if I had only known then what I was saying.

The U-Haul slowed us down from our usual road-trip pace, so we spent one night on the road, sneaking the menagerie into our motel room through the back door. After we arrived in Bozeman around noon, cousin Lee helped us unload most of our belongings into a storage unit with just a minimal amount of our stuff into our short-term apartment.

January 7.

We then drove 750 miles in one day *back* to Seattle, arriving in time for Kelley board her flight to Paris.

January 8.

Finally, we drove a twelve hour, 750-mile, one-day journey *back* to Bozeman to start our new life.

Whew! Driving long distances without stopping is no big deal for us. We made regular mega road trips all over the west with the girls. I loved giving directions from Seattle to Bozeman:

Go south on route I-405

Turn east on I-90

Drive 750 miles

Turn right on 19th street.

These long distance directions were especially common in Montana, as the closest town was usually hours away. Turn right on I-90, drive 3 hours, turn right at Lincoln.

Back to this journey. I had strategically rented an apartment that we would not want to stay in. Yes, I said *not*. Located on a small triangle of land between the highway, airport, and train tracks, it was noisy and would motivate us to purchase a home as quickly as possible.

I found a job right away as an administrative assistant in the International Programs Department at Montana State University. My art career would have to be placed on hold. I had given up any notion of being Annie, or anyone else but Lynne, yet the feeling of empowerment I'd felt exploring who Lynne was artistically was quickly fading into resignation. Now I was "just Lynne."

My job, which called to mind all the international ice skaters who had stayed with us in Seattle, seemed promising. I was working in an office now, so my wardrobe had to change from baggy sweats to baggy dresses. I was comfortable with my clothes.

We knew Alan would quickly find a job, so we wasted no time and started looking for a home to buy. It had always been my dream to live in a city's funky downtown area, and now was the time. Alan kept pushing for a more-for-your-money suburban house, but I was adamant. We had done the suburban thing for the kids' schools and Alan's commute long enough. Now it was my turn.

I found my spot in Bozeman's historic district, an eclectic neighborhood near the university with both mansions and shacks on the same street, and we closed escrow on a wonderful Craftsman home. This home was a hidden gem. I had found it by singling out homes that interested me. I slipped notes into the doors explaining we were looking to buy a home, and *voila!* The owner of this house responded positively.

Our bungalow was located on one of the two streets considered the most historic. It was smaller than most of the other historic homes, so I thought perhaps we could afford it. From the outside it was nothing. It looked small but it had large windows and the perfect location. Once we got into the house, we were blown away. Original woodwork, large rooms, a beautifully remodeled kitchen, and a gorgeous backyard. It was to be ours.

The house also had a full basement with a two-bedroom apartment we could rent out to college students. The attic was huge with room for two bedrooms and a bath, and we planned to make the conversion later that year. The apartment rent would pay for the remodel, but we decided to put off renting and renovating until the girls were back to school in the fall. We wanted to enjoy the summer with them.

We left most of our belongings in the storage unit since the house would be in turmoil for quite a while, furnishing the house just with one sofa, a table, a television and stand, and two beds from our Seattle house. To complete the ensemble, we found a lovely side chair with burgundy-and-beige stripes at a garage sale, and Alan purchased an exquisite over-stuffed chair and ottoman for me as an anniversary present.

My new chair was huge, soft, and squishy, and it could easily sit two adults, or one person could curl up to read or drift off to sleep, enveloped in downy comfort. A fanciful all-over pattern of coral poppies and olive leaves coordinated with the off-white background. It was pure serenity wrapped up in a chair. We placed it in our sunroom. To set off the chair, I painted the sunroom walls a deep coral, accentuating the white trim and built-in bookshelves. It was our bright, sunny getaway.

I was so happy! We had returned to a lifestyle that we set out to have when we were first married—a simple life in a small mountain/ski town. I walked to work at the university, passing young students excited to be living the college life, walked to downtown, getting to know the local storekeepers in beautifully renovated historic buildings, and walked just to walk. I felt good about myself and good about our lives.

After Alan became VP of manufacturing for a local company, he too had a different lifestyle. He went fishing during his lunch, even in the snow (remember, having fun with Alan meant it had to hurt), and we both went skiing when the blue light on the tallest building downtown (three stories) was flashing, which meant that there was fresh powder on the mountains.

We bonded with a group of wonderful couples from the local synagogue, and my mountain mama, hippy self was thriving.

Though I did miss my art.

Kelley and Chelsea arrived the end of May. We spent pleasant evenings in the backyard, surrounded by beautiful trees and chirping birds. The smell of the salmon cooking on the BBQ wafted on the breeze. Children playing soccer in the park behind us reminded us of my time as Chelsea's soccer mom.

"This place isn't bad." Chelsea looked around and smiled.

"Let's go to Yellowstone tomorrow," Kelley suggested. It was only an hour from Bozeman—right in our backyard, in Montana-speak.

The girls seemed okay.

I sighed. We had done it.

I settled into my drab potato-sack dresses and sweats and put my flat chest out of my mind as the summer quickly turned to fall. With the girls back in school, we rented the basement to three graduate students from India. We often spent delightful dinners together, deep in conversation, comparing our cultures and foods.

We began remodeling the house in late October. The plan was to create a staircase at the end of the living room and open up the roof with three dormers to create a new and functional second floor. Through the synagogue, we met our builder, Paul, a soft-spoken six-foot-four man who had moved to Bozeman years ago instead of going to law school. Alan and I were to act as general contractors and do as much as we could ourselves to save money, while Paul guided us through the process.

The first thing we had to do was remove mounds of insulation from the attic. Alan and I donned white one-piece coveralls and full-face masks, and then, using buckets, we began removing the insulation.

"You look like aliens," Jay from downstairs commented.

Alan gave him a small smile and planted a kiss on my mask. He had not been this happy in thirty years. I was right when I called him a salmon; he had returned to his home. His comfort and happiness spilled onto my happiness. My spouse, who had hated his job his entire adult life while trying to keep up with the corporate establishment life, was finally home. I relished the beauty of the environment that we lived in, the mountains, the rivers, and the small town. Life was good.

While Alan seemed to love his new job, I found mine was taking its toll. I was feeling more and more stifled. I was as comfortable with my body as I could be, but inside, I was restless. It was hard for me to conform to a nine-to-five office environment where the most creative decision I could make was whether or not my memos would have borders.

I was trying to find a way to have my creative outlet on the side, but I was becoming more and more depressed because I couldn't put real time into my painting. When I was painting full time in Seattle, my kids gave me a note that said, "You need to paint every day that you eat." I didn't realize how true that was for me. Painting was in my DNA.

"This job is killing you inside," Alan commented one day after work. "Your spark is gone."

Wow! He saw it too!

Maybe it was time to return to my life as an artist.

CHAPTER SEVENTEEN

5:30 p.m., Friday, January 17, 2003

The girls spent the winter holidays with us before Chelsea, our wanderer, was scheduled to fly off to Kenya for her spring semester, two weeks before Kelley had to return to class. It was a lot cheaper to fly out of Salt Lake City than Bozeman, so Kelley and I took this opportunity to drive there with Chelsea and spend a night with Karren.

Alan could not take the time off work, so he said his good-byes to Chelsea at home. He was used to saying "good-bye for now" to her. He planned to fly to Kenya that spring and climb Mount Kilimanjaro with her to celebrate her twenty-first birthday.

"Love you. See you in May." He kissed her good-bye and gave her a huge hug, and I noticed that he was now only a few inches taller than Chelsea. He was getting shorter—and a bit pudgy, which was showing up in his face as well, making his eyes look even narrower, although no less piercing.

He turned to me now for a quick hug good-bye. Even with a few extra pounds, he was still in great shape, still strong. He'd easily shed the weight during that season's mountain climbing and skiing, I figured.

"Drive carefully," he said. "I'll see you Friday around dinner."

We had tickets for a film festival that Friday and Saturday.

"No problem," I said. "I'll see you then. Love you."

They looked so cute, the three of them. I took a photo of Alan with his girls, and I could see his eyes twinkling underneath the tears. He was so proud yet so sad to see Chelsea go.

"Love you, too." Then he hugged Kelley, told her he loved her, and we were on our way.

Normally it was a six-hour drive to Salt Lake, but the roads were icy and snowy so we drove carefully. We enjoyed our staple driving music: Rusted Root, *Dirty Dancing, Havana Nights*, Ricky Martin—only dancing music was allowed on road trips. I think the car bounced as much sideways as forward from our wiggling bodies.

"You have your passport, inoculation papers, phone numbers, ticket, malaria meds, asthma meds, and extra prescription?" I rattled off the list we had gone through so many times that she rolled her eyes as she nodded.

We spent the night with Karren, and then we all went to the airport early the next morning to send Chelsea on her way. Her overstuffed backpack shouldn't have made it through the baggage check, but she flashed her famous smile to the check-in attendant as she coyly played with her curly locks, and somehow the backpack made it.

"How would you like to drive up to Sun Valley and spend the weekend with Gail?" I asked Kelley as we were heading back out to the car. It was a three-day weekend for me, so there was no rush to get home.

"Great idea! But what about your film tickets?"

"I'll call Dad. He could invite Lee or his friend Larry to go."

As I expected, Alan did not mind at all. He knew that I loved Sun Valley and had not seen Gail in a long time. It was hardly out of the way, only an extra six hours, which was nothing. Kelley and I would be home Sunday afternoon.

Gail's daughter had moved to their extended family's

home state of Kentucky, so it was just the three of us. Three silly, giggling girls having a pajama party, except for one brief moment, at 5:30 p.m. Friday, when I felt a quick twinge in my stomach. It was a sharp twist of the stomach that I had never felt before.

Much later I understood what it really meant.

The entire drive home on Sunday, I stewed about my job and decided it was time for me to get back to my artwork full time. I was sure that Alan would support me; he saw what I needed.

"Are you excited to get back to school?" I asked Kelley as we drove through the desolate high-altitude desert of eastern Idaho. We could see the magnificent Grand Tetons off in the distance. The mountains were more ragged than most of the Rockies, and both Alan and I had a special love for them, as we had skied, and he had climbed, those mountains many times.

"I can't believe I'm about to graduate. Everyone keeps asking me what I'm going to do, and I haven't a clue."

"That's okay," I responded while writing a script in my mind of how I would present my desire to quit my job.

We arrived home, and an overexcited Beans greeted us. Alan's cousin Lee was on the sofa, which was no surprise. He was often there. But I did not want him there today because we were tired and I had important stuff to talk to Alan about. We said a polite hello to him, and I looked around for Alan.

"Beans, get *down!*"

Lee stood up and walked over to us.

"Alan is gone," he said, voice cracking. Lee was a big man with a bellowing voice. This was not his voice.

"Gone? What do you mean gone?" I was totally confused and getting more and more annoyed with Beans.

Kelley started to panic. She started waving her arms, wrists flapping about, hopping in place. I wrapped my arms around her while I looked at Lee, still not understanding what he was saying.

"He's g-gone. He had a heart attack Friday." He tried to keep his voice calm and collected, but as our conversation went on, he started to lose control.

"Dad! Dad . . . Dad, where are you?" Kelley pushed my arms away and started jumping around in circles. I grabbed her and held her as tightly as I could. Her long, silky hair melted around her face as her head collapsed onto my shoulder. She sobbed uncontrollably.

"What do you mean?" My grip was getting tighter and tighter. "Beans, get *DOWN!*"

"Alan asked Larry to go to the film festival with him Friday," Lee explained. "Larry showed up and no one answered. The house was unlocked, so he went in and called to Alan, but he didn't answer, so Larry went home. But he kept calling Alan."

Lee's voice quivered as he looked toward the floor, planting his feet firmly to steady his giant torso. "He called Saturday morning, and still no one answered, so he called me. We came over to the house and we went in . . . we found him in the shower. He was gone."

Lee gave a whimper and turned away from us to sit down on the garage sale chair. The chair groaned as Lee's massive body slumped into the cushions.

I held Kelley as tightly as I could. Our arms were twisted around each other's bodies. I was still totally confused.

"We couldn't find you," Lee said. "No one knew where you were, and we had no phone numbers. I called everyone you know in Bozeman, and no one knew where you were."

"We were in Sun Valley," I responded shakily. "I called and told Alan where we were going, but he was the only one who knew."

My thoughts went to Chelsea, on her way to Kenya. How in the world was I going to reach her? I needed to get to Chelsea. *Now.* I needed to hold Kelley. I needed to understand what had just happened.

"Kelley, do you remember where I put Chelsea's contact

information? I know I have her contact information somewhere. Where is it? Where is it? *Where is it?*"

My boss, Norm, knew everyone in the International Study Programs. Maybe he could help me find her. He answered the phone as if he were waiting for my call.

"Norm, can you help me find Chelsea? She is on her way to Kenya. The program is through St. Lawrence University in New York. I have the phone number somewhere, but I can't find it. Norm. Is he really, really, is he really gone?"

I started sobbing uncontrollably.

He already knew what had happened. Everyone in Bozeman knew. Everyone but us.

"I'm so sorry, but yes, it's real," he choked.

Lee took the phone and made arrangements to get Chelsea's number. By now it was late evening on the east coast, but Norm was able to reach the program director at Chelsea's Connecticut college and get the phone number of the school in Kenya. I called the headmistress there. Chelsea had arrived a few hours before and was sleeping. Because of the ten-house time difference, we agreed she'd call Chelsea into the office later in the morning, and I would call and tell her the news.

It was inconceivable to me that this was how my daughter was to hear that her father had died.

What do I do next? This isn't real. I have no experience with what to do next. Next. I don't know what to do next. Hold Kelley. Next. I just saw empty in next.

I made a few of the dreaded phone calls, first to Jann, Karren, and Gail.

I asked Jann to call my parents. It would be too much to tell them.

Jann and Karren would arrive on Monday. My mother and Lauren would come a few days later. My father's Parkinson's disease had advanced to the point where he needed to be in an assisted living home and, with his failing health, he would not understand what had happened to his cherished son-in-law, so it was best to let him stay home. Gail would be up in a few days. We phoned Ty, who went into "I'm not going to deal with the reality of this, but what can I do to help?" mode and phoned more family and friends.

Then Kelley and I sat on the sofa in the empty living room, waiting to call Chelsea. I tried to take in everything that was happening, but I still could not comprehend what was going on. Kelley understood. Kelley always understood. Her life-threatening allergies and illnesses had given her a clear understanding of life and death.

I held her as tightly as I could. Every blanket in the house was wrapped around us. We did not say a word. We just watched meaningless TV shows. I could feel the grief within Kelley's body. My feelings revolved around confusion and worry for my daughters. How in the world was I going to tell my daughter that her father was gone? Over the phone, no less.

We had to make the call in the middle of the night to catch Chelsea at the coordinated time. I held Kelley as I spoke. I heard Chelsea's voice collapse. I felt Kelley's body collapse. I knew our hearts had collapsed. I held Kelley tighter and tighter, as she wrapped her long arms and legs unceremoniously around me. It was all I could do. I wanted so badly to hold Chelsea, but I could not. I could not do anything for her but get her back to me as soon as possible. She was alone. I was helpless.

The headmistress had already booked a flight home, and Chelsea was on her way to Bozeman a few hours later. It had taken her three days to get to Kenya, and it would take her two and a half days to get back. It tore my heart apart to think of her on the plane, all alone. Chelsea's college helped with the plans to get her back to the U.S., which meant that all her college friends knew of Alan's death. One of her friends, who was still home in Wisconsin, drove three hours in the dead of winter to the Minneapolis airport to sit with Chelsea on her layover.

She finally arrived home. I will never forget her face. Jet lag from flying to and from Kenya for six days, along with three days of crying, had made her face so swollen I could hardly recognize her. But I was relieved to have her in my arms. All I wanted to do was hold on to my children.

CHAPTER EIGHTEEN

Care Bears and Casseroles

It did not take long for the house to fill up. Karren and my sister Jann were already here and were talking in a corner, Jann with her back to me but her head turning as she scanned the room, her solid body tensed, clearly ready to take charge if necessary as more and more people arrived. She had very intense brown eyes that seemed to look right through you, but when her gaze fell on me, they softened with such pain that I almost didn't realize I was looking at myself in her eyes.

Four of Kelley's friends from Seattle had piled into an old Toyota Corolla to make the twelve-hour drive, and Kelley's boyfriend and his sister had arrived soon after. Then Chelsea's friend from Seattle came, and my mother and Lauren arrived. The house was a sea of air mattresses with narrow aisles in between. We brought our poppy chair into the living room, where Karren curled up in it. Everyone had fallen asleep, including Kelley and Chelsea, both in my arms. I held on tight, entwined on the oversized sofa, and stared at Karren, snoring away. I wished I could sleep like that. I wished I would wake up and that this would all have been a dream.

The entire town of Bozeman, especially members of the synagogue, was there for me. It was such a strange feeling for everyone to have known before I did. So many people commented that they had seen Alan on Friday, at the local co-op grocery store, outdoors, all around town.

"We were out walking and ran into Alan as he was shoveling the sidewalk," a neighbor commented. "We stopped and chatted. Everything seemed great. He did mention that his shoulder was a bit sore, but after shoveling snow, whose isn't?" No one thought anything of it, not even him.

It bothered me so much that I was the last to know.

But I was so incredibly lucky to have such a support system. In less than a year, we had established close friendships that we had not been able to make in fifteen years of living in Seattle. Our friendships were based on *us*, not built around the girls' activities. My situation would have been very different if he had died while we were in Seattle. I was not alone, I belonged. Finally, I fit in.

I didn't have to worry about feeding everyone. Friends brought over food, tons of food: salads, enchiladas, casseroles and more casseroles.

Kelley, Chelsea, and I bought Care Bear™ stuffed animals to be cremated with him. The kids had always had Care Bears growing up. By sending them with him, he would have us with him. Chelsea picked out her favorite Sunshine Bear, and Kelley her favorite Grumpy Bear. (When she was younger, she would transfer all her pain to Grumpy Bear.) I picked out Love-a-Lot Bear.

Jann took the bears, along with some of Alan's favorite clothes, to the funeral home. His parents, Kelley, and I went to see him to say our good-byes. Chelsea chose not to see him as she had said good-bye before leaving for Kenya. Probably a smart idea. He looked so good, which made it even harder to understand.

The days that followed were a blur, with everyone gradually returning to their lives. After two weeks, Kelley and Chelsea both decided to go back to school. They were certain it was what their dad would have wanted. At the end of the semester, Chelsea would climb Mount Kenya and spread some of his ashes on top. He would have liked that, even though they didn't make it to Kilimanjaro together.

The calls with friends became a familiar routine.

"Anyone but him," they would exclaim with confusion. "He was the epitome of health. A mountain climber, skier, backpacker. He was always so active. He was the last person anyone would think would die of a heart attack."

It was hard to hear and so true. Anyone but him.

I went back to work—probably not one of my best decisions. My house was an empty space, under construction, and I thought it would be good for me to get out every day. It was not. I found myself in a pattern. On Mondays, I was able to make it through a full day at work, but as the week wore on, I was leaving earlier and earlier. By Fridays, I was only able to make it until noon. I cried constantly at the office but found the house, even though it was bare and under construction, to be my sanctuary.

Fortunately, other university employees donated vacation time to me, and I was able to take the time off without loss of pay. I was not making much, but every little bit helped. Bozeman and its population were taking care of me. The town of Bozeman was like that neighbor who had brought the chicken casserole three weeks after my mastectomy. They remembered me.

Paul, our builder, took over the general contracting work until I could think a little more clearly. When I took it back over from him and started calling subcontractors, they would ask, "Are you the lady whose husband just died of a heart attack?"

"Yes, yes, that's me."

"Don't worry. We'll take care of you."

At first I was afraid that taking care of me meant taking all my money, but I quickly learned that they really wanted to help me in my very tough position. That's Bozeman! I belonged.

One day, I came home from work to find a sign outside the mudroom entrance saying, "Don't use this door!" Paul came out looking distressed.

"The floor of the mudroom collapsed," he muttered nervously. "I was walking through it, and it just collapsed. It's completely rotted."

Even though he was standing two steps above me, his six-foot-four frame looked small.

I peered around him and looked at the large hole in the mudroom floor, then looked back at him, dazed. "Okay," I said. "So what do we do?" All I wanted to do was put on my baggiest clothes and go to bed.

"Um, I didn't expect you to be so calm, but this is good. I've already called the restoration company, and they'll be here tomorrow."

"Okay. I'm going to bed now." I retreated into my sanctuary.

It was January. In Montana. Paul helped me put tarps over the three huge holes in the roof that were slated to become dormer windows. It was snowing hard, and the tarps kept blowing off, but they helped a bit. The mudroom was getting fixed.

For the first time in my life, I had no appetite. My friends helped me muddle through each day to get from point A to point B. The basement tenants took turns checking on me, and when they saw that I was having a tough time, they sat with me. For where I was, I could not have been in a better place.

My job was going steadily downhill. I loved the university and the people in the office, but I was going deeper and deeper into depression. One day, as I was walking across campus in a blinding snowstorm, it hit me. Never in a million years did I think I would be a *widow* living in isolated *Montana*.

This was not supposed to happen. Alan was the epitome of a healthy lifestyle, a mountain climber and skier who worked out almost every day and ate healthily.

This was not supposed to happen!

I lay in bed, pondering the situation as the tarps flapped loudly on the roof. Here I was, relatively new to Bozeman, in the middle of winter, a widow with two girls in private colleges, a mortgage, no savings, a low-paying job I was unhappy in, three holes in my roof, no life insurance, and did I mention no husband?

And did I mention I had no boobs?

What the hell do I do now?

CHAPTER NINETEEN

Just Close Your Eyes, Grit Your Teeth, and Do It

I knew I had to do something.

I quit my job at the university to make it as an artist. I had to. As Alan said, this job was killing me. I figured I could always flip burgers at McDonald's if need be. After all, it would not pay much less than what I had been earning at the university.

In addition, I came up with this great plan.

My father, who had been diagnosed with Parkinson's, was unhappily living in an assisted living home in California. It was terribly expensive and the care left much to be desired.

"What if Papa comes up here to live?" I had checked out assisted living homes in Bozeman, and they seemed wonderful—at a third of the prices in California. "It's perfect, Mom. He needs me, and I need him. And you can come up here as often as you'd like because we will be saving so much money. Plus, he can be monitored for his Parkinson's study from Bozeman as well as he could have from California."

Of course, my parents, the clinical trial king and queen, had enrolled my father in a stem-cells study.

My mother and my younger sister Lauren agreed that it was a plausible idea, and after Lauren grilled the home as to the level of care he would need, we made it happen.

I quit my job in May, four months after Alan's death. My father moved to Bozeman. Kelley graduated and decided to spend time in Bozeman while figuring out what to do. Chelsea got a summer internship with a local international nonprofit organization. Ty moved to Bozeman as an ice-skating coach. We would all be together.

We were all catching our breath.

"When do I have to check out of this resort?" my father would ask as he traded off using his walker and riding in his wheelchair while the girls and I took turns pushing him.

"No, Papa," one of us would explain. "This is your home. You can stay here as long as you'd like."

"Good. I like this."

My mother spent weeks with us and hours with my father, now able to just enjoy his company without being drained by the overwhelming burden of his day-to-day care. Kelley and Chelsea helped out with him, and we all took turns spending quality time with him and with each other. It was the perfect solution for everyone.

We decided my father needed a cat to keep him company, so we found a wonderful older cat whose owner, another resident at the home, had died.

"I like that," he said when we mentioned the idea. "I'll name him Nincompoop."

But my father could never remember the cat's name, so we changed it to Pom, which was short for pomegranate because he was as fat as a pomegranate.

Then after only three weeks, the facilities manager called one morning. "Your father needs to leave our facility immediately," she said.

"What happened?" I asked in a daze. She had woken me from an unusually deep sleep. "We moved him into your facility because you assured us that he could stay there no matter what his health was and as long as he wanted. I don't understand."

"The cat is causing problems."

I felt terrible. My father loved the cat, but he needed to stay in this facility, so I would find a new home for the cat.

"That's not good enough," the administrator told me. "Your father needs to leave too. We can't take care of him anymore. He needs to leave immediately."

I was so confused. Why in the world would they kick him out like this? He was a sweet man, we had paid our bill, what was the issue? The confusion would have to wait. They were a private company, so they could do anything they wanted. I would worry about the fight with them later. To this day, after numerous letters to them and the Montana State Office for Health, I was never able to find out why they did this.

Dad loved where he was, and I was sure he was about to be devastated at leaving. Unfortunately, I was right; the move was the beginning of the end of his life. But, at the moment I needed to take care of my father.

I was able to find a great home for Pom, but finding one for my father was not so easy. The choices in Bozeman were limited, but we wanted to keep him here. He was happy, and my mother was flourishing back in San Diego.

The only place that would take him was a nursing home. He wasn't ready for that, but the only other choice was to bring him into my house, which was too dangerous with all its stairs and quirks. We had no choice. The nursing home wasn't pretty, but the care ended up being outstanding; the staff was working there because they wanted to, not because it was the only job they could find, as had been the case in San Diego.

His moving day was sad. Kelley, Chelsea, and I tried to put the best light on it, but my father was confused about why he was leaving his resort. Yet he was a very social man, so he was soon immersed in the small town life of Bozeman, where he became something of a celebrity in town. Everyone knew my father.

We walked with him downtown, and he attended local parades as well as high school and university sporting events. When winter arrived, we found the local ski area had a wonderful program enabling disabled people to ski, and he was by far the oldest person participating. Other skiers considered it an honor to ski with him.

He was out there every week. "Hey, Sid, great day for skiing!" fellow skiers would call from the chairlifts. People would yell and wave to him, and he would beam. Some would stop to sit and chat with him on the outdoor deck, where he enjoyed his usual après-ski meal of chili and french fries.

In the meantime, I was managing to make a living as an artist. My work was happy and light, with lots of color and pattern. My art was my life. Weeks went by without seeing anyone in Bozeman with the exception of my family. My body issues were nonexistent, I lived in sweats with paint spattered everywhere on my clothes. It was safe. I knew that it was safe.

I did venture out when I showed in local galleries and traveled across the country attending art shows. I put thirteen thousand miles on the car in one summer, traveling from Bozeman to California, to Oregon, and to Kentucky, where Gail had moved to be closer to her daughter. The art shows were exhausting, but I was good at them. Kelley, Chelsea, and Ty came with me when they could; otherwise I was on my own. Setup and teardown was a challenge. But I didn't have to flip burgers at McDonald's. I was making it as an artist.

This brought my persistent clothing problem back to the forefront. In Montana, the summers were relatively short. As I traveled to hotter climates, I became increasingly self-conscious. I wanted to look nice, but the less I wore, the more I was of aware of my breasts, or lack thereof; yet the more I covered up, the hotter and sweatier I became. My choices were limited, not only because I was in a small town with few stores, but also because of my body. I wore clothes that were not my style, not me, but somewhat fit the bill to disguise my flat chest and stay in the comfort of neutral dark colors. The thought of wearing a prosthetic was not in my vocabulary. I had tried that before, and the discomfort was not worth the boobs. Or perhaps it was just stubbornness on my part. After all, I was a Montanan now, the land of the independent who would never be told what to do or wear.

In addition to needing new clothes, I needed a new car. I no longer had my Suburban, and our old SUV had over 250,000 miles on it. My car shopping technique was the Cinderella technique: I took a large canvas with me to the car dealerships and bought the smallest SUV the canvas would fit into.

This was car number three. We were unintentionally back to having a car menagerie, complete with another set of "my guys" to handle repairs. I could not bear the thought of selling our old SUV, as it was a connection to our past. The Camry was too small for art shows, and I kept it for the kids.

Home was filling up again. I had three twenty-something kids living with me, I was able to work at what I loved, and almost everyone was healthy. Unfortunately, Beans, our dog, was not faring well. He was a rescue dog that had been abused, and he was now fourteen and in pain. With much sorrow, we had to put him down. Shortly after, Suki, Kelley's cat, had to be put down. With each part of our past vanishing, the pain of losing Alan would be revisited.

But Mona Soup carried on.

CHAPTER TWENTY

Finding me

Bozeman's more mature population seemed to consist of couples who hung out with other couples, or singles at bars. I was neither, so I spent even more time at home. Dating was the last thing on my mind. It had been only 10 months since Alan's death.

I treated myself to a new dog, a Cavalier King Charles spaniel named Tula, but other than walks with Tula and enjoying having my kids at home, my life was that of a hermit.

Then Kelley suggested we take a trip to Paris.

"I know this great hotel," she said, drumming her fingers on her thigh. "We call it Hotel One Star."

My parents had traveled all over the world and my children had lived abroad, yet I had never been off this continent. It really was about time I did.

Hotel One Star was definitely named appropriately. The walls were stained, the bath was so cramped you could barely move, and the ceiling looked as if it would collapse at any minute. The staircase was steep and circular, and only about two feet wide, but each morning and evening we maneuvered it. Lots of doctors were staying at the hotel, which I thought was a good sign. At least we would have medical attention if we collapsed on the stairs.

Our days were filled with walking the streets, visiting museums, sitting in parks, and people-watching. For lunch we bought crepes from a street vendor, and at night we bought cheese and a baguette for about three dollars. Then we'd take our luxurious dinner back to our room and sit on our beds, eating and recounting the day.

The fashions of Paris were spectacular. Even though Kelley was much taller than most Parisians, her looks fit in with the svelte, sophisticated locals. She would pile her long dark hair loosely onto her head and layer odd pieces of clothes together in that sophisticated yet quirky way that Europeans do. Every day I was reminded that my wide potato body did not make the Parisian cut.

"That could be a good look for me, don't you think?" I'd comment, looking at a chic outfit in a boutique window.

"That would be beautiful," Kelley would eagerly respond.

Then we would take a moment to picture me in those clothes. Not going to happen.

They needed breasts. Did I need breasts?

I tried scarves. Every woman in Paris wears a scarf.

I posed. "This look might work for me." It was half statement and half question.

"Scarves would be a great look for you! There are so many ways to wear one."

I purchased a few: two pashminas, one coral and one white, plus a spectacular multicolored one that was a total splurge. I loved the look but found that even the lightweight ones were hot and claustrophobic. Scarves were not going to save this body.

I bought a hat.

My body image was on a roller coaster, but I was not going to admit that to anyone or myself. One day I was proud of my boobless chest, and the next day, awkward and uncomfortable.

By the time we returned from Paris, the travel bug had hit me hard. My art flourished. I was inspired by the sights of Paris and wanted to see more. A year later I jumped at the opportunity to join a group of 16 women on a trip to Portugal. They were from all over the country and some knew each other, some didn't. I knew one person from Bozeman and was looking forward to meeting fresh faces. Perfect! We would be a band of sisters, unconcerned about each other's bodies. I packed my baggy cargo pants, tees, and sweaters, and didn't have a second thought about my body.

I can't remember a moment on the trip when I worried about my body. The women were every demographic and age, but we melded like the band of sisters that we were. We had conversations about life, all of us were in different situations, some stay-at-home young moms, some retired government workers and some type-A overachievers, but it didn't seem to matter what our situation in life was or what our bodies looked like.

We danced with each other in the steamy dance halls of Lisbon, learned to cook a gourmet dinner in the middle of the Portuguese countryside. We visited a medieval village where I met an owner of a tiny gallery who asked to show my artwork at her gallery (Chelsea had advised me to always have a small portfolio of my work at all times). It was an incredible time of making new friends and relishing the splendor of Portugal.

I bought a hat.

The year after that I was off to Peru with Chelsea and my newfound friend, Jill, whom I met on my trip to Portugal. I call these travels my "P" phase. Again, it was a casual, adventurous, and self-reflective trip, so my clothes were not an issue. The three of us white-water rafted down a river in the Andes, saw Machu Picchu, and visited the markets in Cuzco and Lima. In Cuzco we discovered a tiny gallery.

"My mother is an artist, too," Chelsea blurted out with her effervescent smile.

"Really? Let me see your work," the gallery owner replied.

I pulled out my trusty dusty tiny portfolio and again, I was delighted that the gallery owner wanted to represent my work!

The entire trip I was able to ignore any discomfort with my booblessness, blissfully ignorant of how appalled I would be later when I saw my flat, two-dimensional body in the photos.

Chelsea and I had brought some of Alan's ashes with us to spread somewhere in Peru. The girls and I had been and still are spreading them around the world. He's also in India, Kenya, Hawaii, and on his favorite surf beach in Santa Barbara, just to name a few places. Some day we will fly over the Grand Tetons in Wyoming, his favorite mountains, to spread more of him.

We decided to bring the ashes with us to the Machu Picchu graveyard, a flat area above the main part of the village ruins. We put a small amount on the ground and closed our eyes to say a blessing. There was absolutely no wind whatsoever, just dead silence, but when we opened our eyes, the ashes were gone. No one said a word.

Chelsea and I needed time to be alone with our thoughts. I found a small ledge around the corner from the rest of the ruins, with about 3,000 feet of sheer granite cliff below it. I sat down as close to the granite wall as I could, away from the edge, and closed my eyes. A few moments later, when I opened them, five brightly colored parrots were flying right in front of me, no more than twenty feet away. They were as light and graceful as anything could be, in exquisite formation, without a crack in their perfect timing and spacing. I viscerally felt their beauty and freedom.

The Incas believed that odd numbers were good omens. I just knew that Alan was there and happy. I could feel him. Tears came, but not for my loss. I was sad, of course—my husband of thirty years was gone—but I was at peace knowing that his spirit, or whatever you want to call it, was there. He had always needed his nature fix, and he was deep inside it now. He was part of it.

And I bought a hat.

TWENTY-ONE

More Good-Byes

That intense feeling of Alan actually being inside nature became a recurring incident. When Trent's mother visited from Australia over the summer, we headed over to Yellowstone. We promptly became stuck in a long line of unmoving cars.

"Looks like they're doing some roadwork. I think we'll be here awhile."

"I'm going to get out and walk a bit," I told her, my voice uneasy.

She seemed to sense my need to be alone. "No worries," she replied.

As there are no coincidences, we had stopped precisely at one of Alan's favorite fishing spots. I walked along the river until I was completely alone, and then I felt Alan's presence deep in the water. The river was part of him, and he was part of the river. I had experienced this depth of feeling only once before, on the ledge in Machu Picchu, and for the second time since he had died, I sensed that he was okay.

I was having reoccurring dreams about Alan. In them he was confused and trying to figure out why he wasn't with us. Sometimes, he would reappear at our house and I would get really mad at him for coming back. It made me feel terrible and I couldn't understand the meaning within the dreams. Some have suggested that I'm mad at him for going away rather than mad that he was coming back. Perhaps it's a combination— mad at him for leaving and mad that he would play this awful joke on us and try to come back. I was tormented that I was here and he was gone.

Why am I so lucky to still be with our girls and he's not? It's not logical to have this guilt, but it's so hard to shake. Now, alongside the river, alongside Alan, I realized I truly wanted to be alive. It's hard to keep reminding myself that it was not my doing that I was here and he was not, and I wanted to believe that I was here for a reason.

Two years after Alan's death, my father was not doing well. As he aged, the Parkinson's progressed, but we were still able to reduce his medication. My mother and I were certain now that he had been in the study group that had received the stem cells. But this wouldn't be enough to save him.

He was nearing death. He knew it, and we knew it. His death was expected and planned for as well as it could be, so I was dealing with it in a completely different way than I had dealt with Alan's. My mother and Jann came immediately; Lauren had already said her good-byes. We had the local rabbi come in to give my father his blessing.

He had donated his brain to the NIH/Columbia research study, which by now was at least twenty years old. I had been given specific instructions to follow, and it was time for me to make the arrangements. Trying not to think about what I was actually doing, I made the calls to DC and New York. The coordinator needed to talk to the doctor at the nursing home, who needed to talk to the funeral home, who needed to talk to the coroner, who needed to talk to the doctor in charge of the program in New York. It was a complicated coordination, but it looked like we might be able to pull it off.

The study coordinator was a high-energy New Yorker, not accustomed to the laid-back accessibility that was common in a small town like Bozeman. "I've never talked to a coroner in his own home," she exclaimed in her distinctive New York accent. "He said he would be honored to perform the procedure—as long as it didn't interfere with his skiing schedule."

That's Bozeman for you.

We were all able to be with Papa when he died, taking turns napping in a room across the hall the nurses told us to use. He hung on all night, just to keep us up, I'm sure. I sat with him the entire time, holding his hand and telling him that everything was okay. He slept most of the time, only waking up in discomfort when the medication wore off. When I was distracted for a moment, he let go. His breathing stopped. I called everyone into his room but he was gone.

My father, still in charge until the end, had conveniently died at 5:30 a.m., just in time for the coroner to perform the procedure with his brain and get to the mountain for the first run of the day. Papa would have not wanted the man to miss his skiing.

Months later, the doctor in charge of the original stem cell study called both my mother and me. He was giddy with delight as he told us that my father had made history. It had been widely accepted that stem cells would not survive in the elderly population, but the tissue from my father's brain indicated the cells were alive and well at the time of his death. Later the doctor sent us copies of his published book, in which my father was referenced many times.

I missed Papa terribly. I missed Alan. I missed Beans. I even missed Suki. In the three-year period I lived in Bozeman, my life was upended by a whirlwind of loss that I never would have predicted in a million years.

TWENTY-TWO

OMG, the Kentucky Derby!

Needing something to throw my grief into, I poured myself into my art and traveled extensively doing art fairs and shows. As I worked on my art, I discovered that my continuing theme was the distortion of whatever subject I was working on. The more distorted the better.

In high school, I was fascinated with gesture drawings, which use a minimal amount of line to create the feeling of the image, rather than a realistic representation of the image. Now I was returning to that style. My horses were usually in some sort of contorted pose and always had extremely long legs, totally out of proportion, and large hooves. I love large feet whatever the species.

I imposed multiple gesture drawings of horses in different poses and colors over each other and then broke up the spaces with color washes, also on top of each other. The result was beautiful. I was breaking up pattern and color while retaining the movement of each horse. Soon I incorporated women in evening gowns and cowboy boots into the mix. I loved the juxtaposition of the grace and strength of the horse with the strength and grace of a woman in an evening gown—one with the individuality to wear cowboy boots with her gown.

I was often asked what I was trying to say with my work. I hated that question, I just wanted to paint, but my questioners needed to identify a purpose for my work. As I analyzed my intentions, I started to question whether the subject matter and distortions were just superfluous decoration or did they have inner meanings like everyone wanted. I loved the color, the grace, the strength, depth, and individuality of the works. They were complex and required an imagination and study.

At one fair, a lady who had purchased one of my pieces the previous year came to my booth. She confided in me that she was in a dark place when she bought my painting, but the color, complexity and grace of the work helped to pull her out of her funk. She was back to herself, discovering who she was. I found myself sharing my story of breast cancer and realized that it *was* all related. Through my art I was helping others. Hopefully, perhaps even myself?

I wasn't so sure about the "me" part yet.

While I was finding happiness in my art, I was only finding darkness in myself. My art became more colorful while my wardrobe evolved from colorful, twirly dresses and cowboy boots to a sleek, neutral, progressively darker palette.

My traveling increased; I was driving from Seattle to San Diego, from Montana back to Kentucky. I did gallery shows from Montana to Cincinnati and even sent some pieces to Australia. I was earning enough to make a living. I couldn't imagine doing anything else.

From out of nowhere I received a phone call from a woman coordinating an art show in conjunction with the Kentucky Derby. Part of the show's proceeds would go to an organization that rescues ex-race horses. She had seen my artwork online, loved it, and tracked me to one of the Montana galleries showing my work.

I could not believe it. I was invited to present my art at a Kentucky Derby show!

Though of course I'd include some of my paintings, I wanted to do something new for this show as well, something unique that would combine all my interests. The thought of getting my hands dirty while doing three-dimensional work still really appealed to me, so I decided to sculpt a horse. Reflecting my paintings, I sculpted a gestural image of a horse rather than a realistic representation, one with long legs and big feet, of course.

It took two to three months to finish the first horse, and I was working hard on it. When I was done, there were just three weeks before my art had to be shipped, so I challenged myself and sculpted a second horse in those three weeks, working around the clock. The day before my art shipped to Kentucky, I drove 80 miles each way in a snowstorm to get the last sculpture professionally photographed.

These were truly multimedia sculptures, and very different. *Verdigris,* my first three-dimensional horse, is pictured on the sculpture page of my website, LynneHansonArt.com

The horse shape was sculpted with fabric and plaster, and then I completely covered every surface with intricate patterns of minuscule seed beads to create a mixture of patterns and color. The patterns reminded me of Oilily, a creative clothing and accessory company from the Netherlands that always inspires me with its florals and surprising patterns. I'm sure that the intricate beadwork and graphic colors of northwest native American art also influenced my work. Alan loved indigenous art and we had plenty of it in our home.

Beading Kelley's skating dresses had been cathartic and fun when I was recovering from my last mastectomy. Perhaps I hoped the detailed beading would be helpful again as I grieved the loss of another part of me, my father.

Then I faced the task that's always hardest for me: I had to come up with some outfits to wear. The show was in Kentucky at the end of April—hot weather, hot receptions. I needed clothes to keep me cool while they looked hot. A bra and prostheses were not options. I had grown comfortable living without them and was afraid that putting them on again would send me into a sweating stupor.

I had to look great. Not good, but *great.* This was going to be ten times harder than creating the artwork.

I had to recreate *me.*

Bozeman is hardly the shopping capital of the world, so I went online. Orders from everywhere arrived on my doorstep.

"This pile is from Nordie's, this is from Macy's, this is from Breton, and this one is from Anthropologie," I explained to Ty, Kelley, and Chelsea.

"I like this one from Anthro." Kelley held up one after another for me to try on, and then all three voted on which ones they liked. After trying them on, I carefully folded each discarded top into its respective return pile.

They were having a blast, but I was in hell. Trying on clothes in front of three fashionistas was daunting at best, but with only a tank top to protect their fragile eyes from my scarred chest, it was also a lesson in humility. I chose some neutral (surprise, surprise) pieces that had pleated detailing to cover my flat chest. One was a copper-colored sleeveless top that I wore with a pair of tailored black pants. The satin fabric made the copper more colorful than I wanted, but the pleating around the chest and the asymmetrical hemline kept the eye off the chest. The other was a neutral taupe multi-textured knit sleeveless top that came with a flowing skirt and cardigan. I felt pretty good in both of them. They would do.

I had been to Kentucky art fairs before, but this one was in a league of its own. Gail still lived in Kentucky, so she joined me. We stayed at the historic Brown Hotel in downtown Louisville, and Gail upgraded us to a private club floor with its own concierge and refreshments. The perks were totally wasted on me, but I felt so important walking to my room. Most of the Derby festivities had yet to begin, but there was definitely a harbinger in the air of the upcoming events.

This weekend, my time and thoughts were focused on me and my art. I joined the other artists for drinks and meals and helped with the setup. My clothes disguised my lack of breasts and not once did boobs cross my mind. I rediscovered my swagger.

The trip ended up being a fairytale experience. My work got rave reviews and generated twenty-five percent of the art show's total sales. Though Gail and I left Louisville before the serious Derby festivities began, I was thrilled with the show's kickoff. Since the show would continue for the next month, the long exposure for my work would be invaluable.

Twenty-Three

Rowena

Just as I was lulled into thinking my family's lives had settled into a smooth rhythm, Kelley decided to go to grad school in Washington, DC. At the same time, and equally unexpectedly, Chelsea decided to go to law school in St. Paul, Minnesota, and Ty returned to New York City.

Whoosh, I was alone. The short fall days of Montana were quickly turning into the dark days of winter.

The house was empty and I needed a buddy, so I decided to sculpt one. Why not? She would be about four feet tall, her arms spread wide, dancing. Back in my sweatshirt-designing days, I had drawn a wonderful fat ice skater, and my new buddy was sculpted in her likeness. Her rotundness had been very controversial back in the day. It was my subliminal statement of liberation from what was expected: Let the skaters be whatever they want to be! Most loved the design, but there were enough "literals" who thought all ice skaters should be classically (and unrealistically) svelte that the shirts created controversy.

I would put her in my bedroom. She could model my hats.

The only human sculpture I had done was the ugly bust I created years before in Seattle, but I was not worried. I could do it if I just set my mind to it. Of course, it didn't hurt that Jann was a skilled sculptor and could advise me.

I called her from Home Depot. "Hey, it's me." When together, we love to wander its wide aisles to find inspiration

113

and materials, and Jann is an artistic MacGyver. She can figure out how to make *anything*. I didn't see any reason she couldn't do the same over the phone. And I was right.

"I need to find something to form the base of the torso."

"Use the cardboard tubing forms that are used to make concrete columns," she said without hesitation.

That was the first of many such calls, and Jann had all the answers. As I talk with my hands, I could be seen meandering down aisles, waving my arms and seemingly talking to myself as I collected a most unusual assortment of materials.

The core of the torso began with a two-foot-diameter cardboard tube. Added to that was chicken wire, which refined her shape. The bases for her limbs were PVC pipes and her head took form using crushed up aluminum foil, clay, and other miscellaneous items. Rocks from the back yard stabilized her.

"I need something to make the arms rigid."

"Find a medical supply store and buy rolls of fiberglass that are used for casts."

I found lime-green fiberglass at a huge discount. Not skilled in the art of wrapping casts, I never even considered that it might be a good idea to wear gloves. A layer of fiberglass adhered to my hands, making them lime green for days, but the casting material worked beautifully, allowing the sculpture to extend her arms gracefully and gleefully.

I covered the mishmash of materials with layers upon layers of plaster cast material and fabric. Somewhere along the line, my short ballerina grew to be my tall, wide ballerina. She ended up about five-and-a-half feet tall and four feet wide. And flat. Flat as a board.

I painted a black leotard and ballet slippers on her. She was on tiptoes, head cocked just so, sharing her delight in dancing with the world. Her auburn hair was painted on her head in a tight bun. Every once in a while I'd slip a real ballet skirt on her, although I didn't see the need to dress her up. I loved the simplicity of the smooth paint. She did not have facial features—she didn't need them. You could feel her emotion through her posture and position.

I named her Rowena, after a housekeeper we'd had when I was a child. The first Rowena rubbed alcohol on my back whenever I was sick, and she always made me feel better.

TWENTY-FOUR

Signs

Summer was art fair season, which meant once again facing my clothing dilemma. As the temperature increased, so did my anxiety. It was important that I dress as a serious artist, which meant both professional and artsy, but it was also important that I do the physical work required to set up and dismantle my booth in the heat of summer, which meant staying as cool as possible. I began to dread shows because I had to figure out what to wear. Stupid, I know, but it was that important to me.

There had to be other women with this problem. I was a clothing designer and couldn't work with the clothes available in stores—others *must* have an even more difficult time.

The idea of a clothing line lingered in the back of my mind. My art career was going well despite the sinking economy, yet I could feel something calling to me. I am always looking for connections in life and positive reasons for things happening the way they do. I am a percolator, just like the old-fashioned one with a glass top my mother brewed coffee in when I was growing up. I loved watching the water turn from clear to a rich deep brown and listening to the cheery sounds the coffee made as it popped up into the glass lid.

Thoughts, ideas, experiences, and feelings had been percolating inside me. When I had first felt Alan's presence in the river, I had realized I was still here for a reason. Now I was beginning to wonder if that reason, and the reason for my cancer, the mastectomies, the problems with the implant, the clothing struggles—*all* of it—was so I could design a clothing line for women like me.

Since my mastectomies fifteen years before, I had fought the battle to be flat. I was determined that I did not need breasts. After all, my breasts had been so small from the start, and I had always hated wearing a bra. At this point in a woman's life, her breasts sag anyway, more of a nuisance than an asset. I was not interested in dating, so I did not need them to impress a man.

In our misogynistic society, I accept the notion that to be attractive to a man, I need breasts. I call baloney on men who say they will still be attracted to us after we have lost what partially defines us as a woman. (Or am I calling baloney on us women, that it's just our perception that men need us to have breasts?)

We're getting mixed messages. Modern media suggest the bigger the better, and blatantly promote the concept that we need breasts to feel feminine and to attract a man. Wonderful husbands tell their wives they will be loved and desired, breasts or not. For sure, some men always do desire and love their wives, no matter what happens to their bodies. Yet men's actions tell us that we need breasts.

I did not need my breasts for breastfeeding. I did not need them at all. Or even want them. But I *did* want to look good. I wanted to look like a three-dimensional, feminine woman. If you look at fashion magazines and fashion illustrations, a women's body is most feminine in an "S" shape, whether looking at the body from the front or the side. In the full frontal view, the female body creates a "S" shape, breastless or not, but from the side, the "S" is lost if there are no breasts.

I thought, no, I *knew* without hesitation that there must be other women like me, who have had mastectomies or who were naturally flat. They still wanted to feel and look feminine.

I was a clothing designer, for God's sakes! I could create this! Nothing had ever seemed clearer to me. The signs were all there. The newspapers seemed filled with stories of celebrities having mastectomies. Another sign. Choosing mastectomies without reconstruction was a growing trend.

Women all over were facing the challenge of losing what our society defines as their femininity. My mission would be to help them feel confident and beautiful no matter what shape or lack of shape their cancer had left their breasts in. Oprah would embrace me as the one who had changed everything. All of womankind would applaud me for liberating them.

Why did it take me so long to come to this epiphany? It had been a long journey of ignoring the issue and trying to talk myself into not caring. But I do care! Others care! Now was the time. All the signs were aligned.

I even had the perfect name for the line: *Annie Flats.* This was why that name was in my life, and why it had been so important for me to keep it when I bought out my partner. Back then, I had assumed it mattered because it was a family name, but now I was certain that I had been emphatic about it so that I would have it for this moment. Annie would be back in business, and so would Flats.

My idea was twofold. First, I would design the clothes with specific needs of women like me in mind. I would use myself as both market and fit model. If I would wear it, it would work. The premise behind the designs was to use fabrics and detailing to confuse the eye, so that what was actually beneath the clothes would be vague. This was so easy.

Second, I would launch a campaign to educate women on *going flat* or *natural* as a positive alternative to dangerous implants or uncomfortable prostheses. Annie Flats would send a message of strength, confidence, and beauty. I am not sure whom I was trying to convince, other people or myself, but it did not matter. This campaign would become my life's obsession.

This was my noble cause. I would be the Mother Teresa of boobs . . . rather, of no boobs.

One minor problem. Sewing. My blood pressure goes sky high when I sit in front of a sewing machine. I had been a good patternmaker in my day, and I knew how to sew, but my craftsmanship was terrible. I needed my priceless creations to be perfect. I needed to find help. But try as I might, that help was not materializing in Bozeman.

This only contributed to a growing uneasiness with my life. Although I adored Bozeman and the house I had worked so hard to stay in and finish, I was alone. Rowena alone just was not doing it for me. Bozeman seemed to be a town of couples and young adventurers. I was neither. Well, maybe an old adventurer.

I clicked with one woman, Birdie, who coincidentally was from DC, not far from where I had grown up. Her daughter was attending graduate school in Bozeman, so her family had purchased a vacation home there. Whenever she was in town, we would explore garage sales together, and whenever I was in DC visiting Kelley, we would make time to get together.

With the exception of Birdie, I was a hermit, concentrating on my artwork and planning my clothing line. Days would go by without seeing anyone, and in the back of my mind was the knowledge that Alan had died alone and the uneasy thought that if something were to happen to me, no one would find me for days.

I got into the habit of calling Jann first thing every morning.

"Still alive" was the only thing I needed to say.

Someone needed to know that I was still breathing.

I decided to move to Colorado Springs, where Jann had her ranch. I needed her now, and I liked to think that she needed me—as family, as a friend, as a yak herder. Yes, she had added yaks to her menagerie.

In Colorado, I could work on my clothing line and be safe.

I still loved Bozeman and did not want to give up the dream completely, so I would try to hang on to the house. As an added bonus, Colorado Springs had a world-class ice-skating program. I would find my patternmakers and sample sewers from the many skating costume makers there.

Another sign!

TWENTY-FIVE

The Next Leap

On an early spring morning, I headed out of Bozeman to start the next phase of my life. It had been just over five years since Alan and I had arrived there to live out our dream. I'd rented the house to tenants who would treat it like their own, I hoped. The movers packed up Rowena and all my boxes and belongings and were on their way. I packed the most fragile of my possessions into my car and headed off to Colorado Springs with Tula and Mona Soup.

I was a road trip veteran. I had my pretzel rods, twenty-ounce bottles of Pepsi, and my stock traveling music—with the recent addition of the soundtrack to *Shall We Dance*.

It was snowing lightly, but the forecast had not mentioned anything unusual. In Montana, only a raging snowstorm, at the very least, is weather to worry about. Two hours into the trip, it started snowing harder, and by four hours it was a full-blown blizzard. I stopped in Sheridan, Wyoming, to get gas and found out that all roads and highways had closed. I was stranded.

There was a long line in the lobby of the Super 8 Motel. People were friendly but apprehensive. All of us needed a place to stay, and there were only a finite number of hotel rooms available.

"Which way are you going?" asked the guy in front of me, a tall, burly man in a FedEx uniform.

"South," I replied. "But not today. Which way are you going?"

"North. I'm driving that truck out there in the parking lot." He gestured toward the lobby window. I could barely make out the shadow of a huge FedEx truck. The snow and wind had picked up considerably. I thought of my little SUV, packed to the brim, with a dog and cat waiting inside, and hoped it wasn't buried already.

"FedEx reserved a room for me, but now they're telling me to keep driving," he said. "I don't know if they realize how bad it is, but corporate says to drive, so I'm going. I was just standing in line to give it up, but if you'd like, I'll give it to you."

Wow, what luck!

"I'd love that! Thank you so much. And if you do have to turn around, I'll be happy to share it with you." That was the least I could do, and only fair, I thought. This man seemed like a harmless gentle giant. I'd take my chances.

The front desk clerk announced that all rooms were booked, so the driver and I stepped forward, and I was given his room.

I smuggled the pets into my room through the back door. I didn't want to take the chance of asking if I could bring them in. If the clerk said no, I couldn't leave them in the car to freeze, and every other hotel in town was booked. I had been planning on making the trip in one long day, so I'd brought no provisions for Mona. I had to take my life into my hands and drive to the K-mart a few doors down to pick up some cat food, kitty litter, and an aluminum baking pan for a kitty litter tray. By the skin of my teeth, I made it back to the hotel, sort of walked the dog, and settled in for what I thought would be one night.

Wrong. The snow didn't stop. The roads didn't open. In the midst of the next big leap in my life, I was suddenly frozen in midair.

My FedEx guy had been turned around and was back at the hotel. Somehow he had been able to get a room. I lined up with the other guests to rebook my room, and when some mentioned that the Subway was open, a bunch of us headed out to scrape the snow and ice off our cars and try to navigate the snow-packed, icy local streets.

The FedEx man was sitting in his truck, eating a sandwich and reading. "Have you found the Subway?" I asked.

"No, I can't drive this big rig around the city streets," he said. "I walked over to the gas station across the street." He motioned toward a solid sheet of snow. "They had some prepackaged sandwiches, but they're running out."

"I think I can get out," I said. "Why don't you come with me?"

"Sure, sounds great." He jumped out of his truck, locked it up, and we headed toward my car. He had to contort himself to fit into the passenger seat.

The narrow city streets were lined with piles of snow, abandoned cars, parked cars, and fallen tree branches. The snow was coming down hard, and my windshield wipers had trouble keeping up. We had to keep stopping to wipe away the heaps of snow weighing them down. Every time, after he got out to wipe away the snow, my gentle giant had to figure out how to get back in, trying new ways of squishing his large, wet body into the cramped front seat.

The sandwiches were delicious, but after three days of this, Subway got a bit old. Each day, we would line up to rebook our rooms as we found out that the roads were closed for yet another day.

Tula needed to be walked, but it was a precarious and short adventure because the snow had piled up several feet higher than her head. A few other people had pets, all of us hiding them in our rooms and keeping quiet. As we walked through the halls, we would nod to each other knowingly.

I was running out of food for the animals, having bought the smallest possible bags at K-mart that first day, thinking we'd be in Colorado the next, so my Fed Ex buddy and I headed over to the grocery store across from the Subway after lunch, walking in to the most bizarre sight. The entire store was just about empty, and I'm not talking about people. There was hardly anything on the shelves. Delivery trucks had been unable to get through and the town was an isolated, overpopulated island full of trapped travelers. When I spotted some dog and cat food, I felt as if I'd hit the mother lode.

The movers had left ahead of the storm, and they made it to Colorado Springs before the roads closed. While I watched *The People's Court* on my hotel bed with a dog and confused cat jumping around me, I directed Jann in placing my furniture.

"Have them put the red hutch in the living room. I want it by the fireplace."

"It doesn't fit next to the fireplace," said Jann. "It's about three inches too big."

"Okay, let's try the wall across from the fireplace. Tula, stop terrorizing Mona! Put Rowena by the picture window. She'll enjoy the view."

"Call you back."

Finally, on the fourth day, the interstate opened. Throughout my life, whenever something new starts out bad, it ends up great. If this strange luck still applied, my new life was definitely going to be amazing.

Jann had set up my new townhouse beautifully. The large living room was now my airy studio, with vaulted ceilings, a fireplace, a magnificent view of the Rockies, and with southern light filling the room. An indestructible floor cloth that Kelley and I had made covered the pecan-stained wooden floors. Two dining tables pushed together made one huge worktable. The red hutch held my art supplies, and I'd found two ornate chandeliers which filled the room with even more light.

The dining room was now my living room. French doors led to a patio, where I would spend my evenings percolating plans for my new life while looking out on the mountains.

Rowena moved around the house from window to window, confusing my new neighbors as to what or who she was.

I signed up for ballroom dance lessons. They were on my bucket list, and I was on a roll. This was going to be tricky, however; whenever a partner held me, I worried that he wondered where the boobs and bra back were. After all, these men were used to putting their arms around a woman's body. I'm sure that they've felt every sort of lump, bump, and strange body imaginable. But have they ever felt *nothing*?

And even more important, why the hell do I still obsess over this?

Get over it and dance, I told myself. I don't know why that's easier said than done, except that I care far too much what *I* think others are thinking of me. This is ironic, because I often tell my kids, sisters, family, and friends, "People are far too busy thinking about what they themselves look like, how they behave, etc. to worry about you." Why can't I take my own advice?

The lessons were fun, but too often I felt like a pathetic, old, deformed lady who had to pay a gigolo. I valiantly attended the "socials," where the few male dancers would make the rounds, dancing with the women without partners.

Women without partners—sounds like a support group.

I pushed myself to go to a dance seminar. I marched into the studio, proud of myself, sticking out my chest to show the world that I was woman. It was an instinctive move. Or was it? Our breasts are our peacock feathers. Have we been genetically programmed to use our breasts to attract a man, or is it learned?

"You, in the brown shirt," the instructor twanged. "Hon, come on over here and show everyone what *not* to do with their posture. You're doing it so well."

It is going to be a while before I take dance lessons again.

Twenty-Six

Women without Partners

L ife became quiet. At least as quiet as my restless soul
would allow.

"Mom, you need to start dating," blurted Chelsea.

We were walking along the beautiful, tree-lined streets of
St. Paul, where Chelsea attended law school. I loved to visit
her as often as possible. I could tell that she had been working
up the nerve to say this, and it had just come out with the
intensity only Chelsea could muster.

Life with Chelsea was always a statement, not a question.

She was never one to mince words, or to talk just for the sake
of talking, so the silence that followed was not unexpected.

Then she added gently, "Dad's been gone for a while now,
and I think it's time for you to date."

More silence.

"Why do I have to date?"

"You need new friends and need to get out and do things."

"I have friends, and I do things."

"But you need to date."

"I'll think about it. I love you."

I wasn't interested in dating, but maybe I would give
dancing another try if I could find someone to dance with. I
decided to try to find my dancing soul mate.

I signed up for J-Date, an internet dating service for Jews. I
figured that at least my dates and I would have something in
common, being Jewish. Also the dating service would help prevent
my friends from feeling pressured to find dates for me. If a date
didn't work out, there wouldn't be any hard feelings. Perfect.

So I signed up and let the service find my perfect matches. First one—a woman in her sixties. Whoops. I'm pretty sure I'm not a lesbian, but maybe the Internet knew something I didn't. Besides, I was only fifty-eight. Why couldn't I go out with some young chick?

My experiences with internet dating never did include a date with another woman, but there were many, many disastrous first dates.

One man seemed very nice—intelligent and not bad looking. We emailed a few times, then I let him phone me. We chatted a bit. He had two dogs he loved, and as Karren had told me, any man I dated should have a pet and kids, so he seemed like a good candidate. We set up a meeting at a park not far from Kelley and Jack's condo in DC, where I was visiting. We would bring our dogs, let them play at the park, and then go out for lunch. This sounded safe enough.

First red flag. He kept telling me that he was going to bring me flowers. Well, I love flowers as much as anyone, but let's not think that flowers will conquer the world. Or the woman.

It was important to me not to hide my flatness. I didn't want to flaunt it in his face, but I didn't want to hide it either. Luckily, it was spring, so I could pretty much wear whatever I wanted. Since we were going to a park, I dressed in my comfortable-yet-not-sweats cargo pants and roomy cashmere sweater, with a T-shirt under it. Going on a date was already way out of my comfort zone, so dressing comfortably was crucial to me.

I arrived at the park a bit early and let Tula off her leash to play fetch with her ball. Not long after I arrived, I saw a small man walking toward me with an adorable dog and a very sorry-looking, crumpled, dying bunch of flowers wrapped in an old plastic grocery bag. The flowers looked like they'd come from someone's garbage, but hey, he was nice enough to bring flowers, so I'd give him a chance.

"Do you like the flowers? See, I brought you flowers, what

do you think of them? I told you I'd bring you flowers, and look, here they are. Just as I said I'd do. What do you think of them?"

I was speechless.

"Thank you so much. They're very pretty," I responded politely.

"Here, take the flowers. I told you I'd bring you flowers, and here they are. What do you think of them?" He insisted. He was a journalist, so maybe he was just trained to get to the truth. But that was the last thing I was going to tell him.

"They're very nice. Thank you so much," I responded as he shoved them in my face.

I put Tula's leash down and took the old, wrinkled grocery bag with the wilted flowers. They were past their glory days and were begging to be composted.

"Your dog is so pretty. What's her name?" I asked.

"Mandy." Period.

"How old is she?"

"Seven." Period.

"My dog is five."

Silence.

"What exactly do you do for a living?" was the next question that came to my mind.

"I'm a journalist." Period.

This conversation wasn't going anywhere, and neither was this date. I asked a few more questions and then decided that I was sick of this game, and we threw the ball for the dogs in dead silence.

"Shall we go get lunch?" I asked. "I saw a nice restaurant in Georgetown with outdoor tables around the corner, so we can take the dogs there."

"Yes. We can put your flowers right in the middle of the table." Well, at least I got a few more words out of him. He must be a lousy journalist, I thought. Or maybe he's a good one, the way he just picks one topic and obsesses about it until you're worn down.

We walked a few short blocks to the cozy sidewalk cafe and found a tiny round table close to the pedestrian traffic. There wasn't much room between tables but it was quaint.

"Put your flowers right here, right in the middle of the table." I had placed them at my side because there was no room on the table, but I put the floppy flowers right smack in the middle. Happy?

Each of us ordered lunch, and the poor waitress could do nothing right.

She came out with glasses of water and some bread and butter. There was no room, so I moved the grocery bag toward me, and she squeezed the glasses and bread bowl onto the table.

"I want more ice in my water," he demanded. My pet peeve is when people don't say please and thank you. At first he was just harmless and annoying, but now I was starting to fume.

"I don't like that type of bread. I want another type," he continued to quibble.

"The salad has too much dressing on it. The sandwich is too hot. Do you like the flowers, aren't they beautiful? What do you think of the flowers? Where are you going to put the flowers when you get home? Aren't they beautiful? Well, what do you think of me? Do you like me? What are we going to do next?"

I took a deep breath and couldn't look him in the eye. I looked down at Tula and his dog, who had been dutifully sitting by our sides, waiting for a crumb to fall.

"You seem very nice," I stuttered.

"Honestly, you can tell me. What do you think of me? You can be honest. Tell me."

"I just don't think we have anything in common." This was the kindest thing I could say. I expected him to continue to question me about himself, or to at least ask me how I liked the flowers, but instead he jumped out of his chair, jerking his poor dog up by the collar. She flew through the air as he knocked his chair over.

"Well, I guess I'm just an asshole," he yelled as he ran out of the table area. He was across the street and into a cab before I could even start to comprehend what had just happened. I was speechless. The customers eating next to us stared at me with disbelief. What in the world had just happened? I was shaking. Luckily, we had already paid (we'd split the bill), so I tried to collect myself, grabbed the sorry flowers for some reason, and with a confused Tula, shakily walked home.

The profiles of the men in DC were more interesting than the ones in Colorado, for some reason. There was one intriguing match: Ben. He'd had a very successful PBS political interview show for more than twenty-five years, had written many political books, and was considered a bit of a celebrity in DC. He was witty, self-deprecating, and funny. Unfortunately, he was also extremely forgetful, forgetting my name and my situation time after time. He just wanted to know that I was a woman, and after one date, when I would marry him. Perhaps when I got older I would become interested in a situation like that, but at that moment, marrying a man who could not remember my name was not on the agenda. I admit, he does still have a special place in my heart.

Internet dating became a sport of sorts. At night I would spend hours looking at profiles (it's an amazing time waster), sometimes saving them as favorites, sometimes reaching out to them. I needed to not take the sport too seriously because the responses were so bazaar and sporadic. Most of my matches eventually either ghosted me after a week or so, or ended up being one of my endless "first coffees." I think I should qualify for the award for the most first coffees, and I can hang it right next to my award for the most second opinions for my cancer options.

After I met a prospect for coffee, the interest was usually nil and I'd move on to the next guy. The most annoying and inevitable question was "Have you had any luck with internet dating?" *Of course I didn't, you idiot! If I had, do you think that I'd still be here!?*

During another visit with Kelley, I met a man whose

profile picture depicted a vibrant upper-middle-aged man who reminded me of my father, both his class and his grace. Wearing my go-to date sweater and jeans, we met at the Beaux-Arts Union Station, the train station adjacent to the Capitol Building. I caught a glimpse of him out of the corner of my eye and my heart sank. At least 40 years had been added since the photo.

My first thought was, *Do I leave?* I wanted to *so* badly. Yet I couldn't do that to someone, but, oh, how I wanted to.

It turned out to be a very illuminating couple of hours SLOWLY walking around the Capitol listening to a one-way conversation. Turns out that my date is a very enlightened man who keeps a "board of directors" available for him to talk to whenever he needs advice.

"That's great," I managed to get in two words.

"Who is on your board?" Five words!

Expecting to hear names of friends of his that I didn't know, or perhaps a person in the current spotlight, I was kind of interested in knowing who in our world he respected enough to have on his "board of directors."

"Well, Gandhi is my chairman of the board."

Okay . . . .

"Then there is General MacArthur, Franklin Roosevelt, Genghis Khan and, of course, Albert Einstein."

HMMMM.

"Do you actually talk to them?"

"Yes, I channel them whenever I need advice."

I can guarantee you that at this point, my breasts or lack of thereof was the last thing on my mind. As a matter of fact, I was ready to bare my ugly scars to him just to scare him away.

Sorry, Chelsea.

Mom doesn't want to date.

But the idea of having a board of directors is certainly an interesting one.

TWENTY-SEVEN

Patience, Prudence

I had better luck meeting new friends than meeting dance partners or dates. I met Carolyn when I volunteered at a local ice-skating competition, and we became instant walking buddies. It was an unlikely match. She, the epitome of class and elegance, was always dressed immaculately, her hair coifed, with perfect makeup, and I was usually wearing my baggy cargo pants and faded cashmere sweater, with a bit of makeup here and there.

I came into Carolyn's life as she was losing her husband to a prolonged illness. I seemed to be what she needed at the time, just as she was what I needed. Our backgrounds were as different as night and day, but we were connected from the start. Thanks to my many moves, I've learned the people who come into our lives are there for a reason. The reason might be theirs or mine—it doesn't matter. In Carolyn's case, the reason probably belonged to us both.

One day Tula and I were strolling down a lovely street when a car drove by, stopped, and started backing up. The driver was about my age, and she looked sane, even though she was excitedly waving her arms at me.

"I have the same breed of dog!" she exclaimed.

You have to understand that Tula's breed is not the usual western mountain dog. Seeing another King Charles Cavalier, especially in the mountains of Colorado, is like seeing a long-lost friend. The lady introduced herself as Linda, and her dog as Lucy. We chatted for a while on the side of the street, and she invited us to her home, around the corner, to meet her dog.

Tula and Lucy greeted each other with the familiarity of cousins, and we all spent the next few hours with our new buds. After that, every Monday we met and had great walks with our dogs. Tula developed a girl crush on Lucy and knew the way to her house from ours. I think if she ever got lost, she would have headed to Lucy's house, not mine.

Linda owned Saboz, a downtown shoe and accessory store. She had lived in Colorado for many years and was well connected with the businesses in town. She was eager to help me find a sample maker for my fledgling clothing line, and she introduced me to Jan, owner of Janska, a small clothing company. Jan specialized in jackets for disabled adults, such as those confined to a wheelchair, as well as people going through chemotherapy. Her jackets were well-designed and made of Polartec, a practical and warm fabric.

Jan and I were interested in each other's concepts. She didn't know anyone who could help me, but she asked if I would be interested in helping her take her line to a more fashion-forward place, because they were looking to get into more upscale boutiques. Fantastic. I could use the money and Janska's connections could help me with my line.

I had always been the type of person who needed to have things done yesterday, but this time I was going to be different and let things happen organically. Patience would be my new mantra.

Little did I know that my sister, Jann, and I were about to be taught a new lesson in patience.

One day as I was about to leave my house to meet an old skating friend who was in town for a competition, Jann called. "I need you," she said frantically.

"What's up? I'm about to leave for lunch." I was a bit annoyed. She knew I had been looking forward to seeing my old friend.

"The yaks have escaped."

Yaks, I have learned, are nasty, strange creatures; they look like a horse, cow, pig, and longhorn, all rolled up together into one odd body.

Jann had wanted some animals to graze her mountain property, and yaks didn't require much attention (or so she had thought). Plus, she could sell their hair to weavers. Jann never does anything lightly, so instead of getting one or two yaks, she got eight. And one was pregnant. Yaks are not agreeable at any time, but especially not when pregnant or when they have a baby to protect.

And did I mention that they have pointed horns that extend at least a foot out of their skulls? I kept bugging Jann to put tennis balls on the ends of their horns to protect herself from being gored, but she never even got close enough to try.

"Where did they go?"

"We think they are near a neighbor's ranch."

When the neighbor woke up and saw eight yaks outside his front window, he called a neighbor who called a neighbor who called Jann. Definitely not a normal sight in the Rocky Mountains.

"We need to go up there and try to catch them or something."

"Something" being the operative word. The yaks were not about to let anyone catch them.

I sighed and rubbed the bridge of my nose. "I'll cancel my lunch and be ready to go."

We found them grazing near the horses on a neighbor's ranch. On one side they were bounded by a fence with a small gate; there was nothing on the other three sides but miles and miles of open land. They were free to go absolutely anywhere in the vast Rocky Mountains.

This was going to be a challenge. There were seven of us—including Jann, me, my nephew's girlfriend, Jann's ranch hand, and the neighbor up in the mountains—trying to catch eight nasty, aggressive thousand-pound beasts. *This* should work.

We decided to somehow herd the yaks toward the gate.

First, we built a small pen in front of the gate by latching sections of portable metal fencing together. If by some miraculous chance we were able to get the yaks into the pen, we could take out sections to make it smaller and smaller, forcing the yaks into Jann's horse trailer, which was parked with the back ramp open at the gate. This was a great plan with one major flaw. How in the world would we get all the yaks, at one time, into the pen?

Most of us were on foot, and the neighbors had two all-terrain vehicles. The plan was for us to get behind the yaks and slowly move forward to push the yaks toward the pen, where we piled lots of hay to tempt them. The wild grass wasn't that good, so hopefully they would be tempted by the hay.

We had to circle *way* beyond the yaks to get around them, because they could run away from the pen at any time they felt threatened. Slowly, very slowly, we moved in. We had at least 100 yards between each of us, so it would have been easy for any of the yaks to gallop between us and away from the pen. We would have never seen them again.

But somehow, it worked. It took a long time, but we were patient, and the yaks were hungry. We were able to get them into the pen, and slowly, as they calmed down, we would carefully remove a section of the fence. There was even more hay in the trailer, and for some joyous reason, they all climbed peacefully into it. We quickly closed the gate to the trailer and thanked the neighbors profusely for their help.

A neighbor commented about it being nice to finally meet Jann's big sister, which I didn't bother to correct because one, we were in a hurry to get the trailer of yaks back to Jann's ranch, and two, I was getting used to it. I had a couple of inches on Jann and way more than a couple of gray hairs. Her wavy brown hair was barely starting to gray. Everyone assumed she was younger than I was.

This experience soured Jann on her yak-keeping experiment,

and she soon sold them. She had finally met her match. And I added yak herding to my resume.

Between helping Jann on her ranch and working on Janska's line, I hadn't done anything with my own clothing project. It was time to get on with my mission.

I had not yet found my perfect patternmaker, so I decided it was time to do some patternmaking of my own. After all, I used to work as one, albeit thirty-five years ago, but I was good at it then, and I could be good at it now.

In addition to the pattern making tools, I needed to have a dress form that replicated my body. It would be used not only for draping garments, but also as a tool on which I could try out design ideas. Dressed in my oldest sweatshirt, sweatpants, and assembling my massive array of saws, I was ready for surgery. I was astonished at how much I needed to saw away from the dress form to recreate what was taken away from me.

I was removing more than just the breast. I was removing the grief of losing my breasts, the grief of losing my husband, the grief of losing the life we had dreamed about for over thirty years. The cavernous hole exposed the inner body. Me exposed—to the air, to the world, to myself.

It needed to be closed up quickly.

Fabric strips, plaster, bandages, anything that I could find went into covering the hole. But it had to be right. I mapped the convex and concave nuances of my chest to get just the right form.

"This is crazy. It can't be concave, but it is." Tula and Mona stared at me. They understood my pain.

I gently pulled an old T-shirt from under Mona. It was warm and gave me a sense of comfort. I slid it over the dress form and the exposed damage was snuggled under the soft knit fabric and ready to save the world. Or at least start a conversation.

At first I purchased ready-made patterns from the fabric

stores, hoping to simply alter them for my purposes. Much to my disappointment, they did not work. The disfigured body of a mastectomy patient was different from a breast-toting body, even a tiny-breasted breast-toting body. Fabrics draped differently. It did not make sense, but my dress form proved it true. I drew, draped, drafted, and pulled out old patternmaking books.

I even sewed.

TWENTY-EIGHT

Vamoose

As I struggled with the patterns, I knew I also needed to find "the" wonder fabric that could hold a shape while still being soft and natural, cool yet warm.

New York was the place to go.

In New York, I would search for my fabric. In addition, I planned to meet with potential resources for Janska, as they were looking to move their manufacturing to a larger facility, attend Ty's ice-skating show, and see family. Then I would head down to DC to see Kelley.

I love New York. When I was growing up, we visited our relatives in New York on a regular basis. I knew the city pretty well and thought that it would be a breeze living there. But as a product of suburbia, I found myself to be painfully naïve and unprepared to be a struggling, starving art student. I fled New York, feeling overwhelmed.

Thirty-five years later, I embraced the vibrancy of the city. I wandered the streets of the garment district, in awe of the endless aisles of fabrics from around the world. Within hours, I found my wonder fabric. This was so easy; it was meant to be! Another sign. The fabric was made from bamboo, soft and cool for those of us still dealing with hot flashes, and it was a sustainable "green" fabric to boot. Perfect. I bought a few yards and held my dreams in my arms.

Then I met with Remi, a potential resource for Janska. China was the place to have garments manufactured inexpensively, but there could be many complications, so they were looking for a middleman they could trust.

"Trust me," Remi kept saying. "I can make anything happen for you." The repetition got old.

In the end, Janska stuck to their grassroots program and continued to manufacture in the United States.

When in New York I treat myself to two very special meals. The first is at a hole-in-the-wall Chinese restaurant that makes the most incredible soup dumplings I ever tasted. I could live on them. The other is a corned beef sandwich from Carnegie Deli. Yes, it's touristy and fatty, but such a treat. I picked up one to eat on my bus ride to DC.

The buses from New York to DC are inexpensive and sometimes can be sketchy. One of the first was the Downtown bus, which was known for its irregular schedule, breakdowns on the New Jersey Turnpike, and drug busts. New bus lines were popping up all the time, and I booked a seat on Vamoose, one of the newer companies.

From the outside, the bus resembled a rock star's traveling machine, right down to the black-tinted windows. Sandwich in hand, I was welcomed at the bus door by the driver, John from Russia.

"Free soda for all students," John greeted everyone in his heavy Russian accent. "You need the caffeine to study. Not a student? Here, have a soda anyway."

I sat in a row by myself, three rows behind the driver's seat. John continued to hand out sodas to the students, whose study habits concerned him. I loved John. I loved this bus. I had never been happier.

"What movie would all of you like?" John asked enthusiastically. "We have *The Gladiator* or *My Big Fat Greek Wedding*. You want *Big Fat Greek Wedding*? Good. That's the one I want too."

The bus got rolling, and I settled in for my adventure with an unobstructed view of the little TV screen above John. We passed the disgusting oil refineries, then got on the New Jersey Turnpike. Poor New Jersey. It gets a bum rap. It's actually a beautiful state, but not many people get beyond the initial yuck to see how lovely the rest of it is. Maybe that was for the best; it might stay beautiful.

I was feeling content, almost elated. I had found my wonder fabric, had seen family in New York, was heading to see Kelley, and was eating a Carnegie Deli sandwich while watching *My Big Fat Greek Wedding*. What could be better?

I was engrossed in the movie when the bus suddenly pulled over to the median and stopped. At this point the turnpike had only a three-foot-tall cement barricade between us and the masses of oncoming cars. John got out of the bus. Was Vamoose breaking down like the infamous Downtown bus? We waited in silence.

Then John returned to the bus. "My glasses blew out the draft window." Then he got in his seat, closed the door to the bus, and started backing up, on the left shoulder, into lots of oncoming traffic—and without his glasses.

This is the end. I am going to die. But I can't die. I have breastless women to save!

He stopped the bus again and got out. Either we would die or John would, and we would be stuck here for eternity.

Then he was back, waving the glasses and smiling ear to ear. They were intact! He fastened his seatbelt and off we went.

The bus was silent.

TWENTY-NINE

With a Little Help from the Pros

Washington, DC was fun and allowed me to regain my sense of focus. When I returned to Colorado Springs, I was ready to leap into my obsession.

Linda introduced me to Gabrielle, a French seamstress and who was soon to become my savior. Linda knew her to be an excellent pattern maker and custom seamstress. That was exactly what I needed! I could design, I could fabricate, I could even do the patterns. I draped designs on my lovely dress form (by now we had become friends) and drafted patterns to create the initial design concept. But having a pro to help with the patterns and do the sewing was a godsend.

Gabrielle arrived in a huge car—Joan of Arc in a Cadillac. She was in her seventies but looked younger, with bright red coiffed hair and flawless makeup. Maybe too much makeup and a bit too colorful, but perfectly applied. She wore beautifully made form-fitting clothes in bright colors and lots of matched jewelry. Her heavy French accent completed the package.

I had donned my favorite baggy cargo pants, a form-fitting tank top, and the oversized pink striped shirt that used to house my hamster. No makeup. I was the serious artist, too busy to worry about my looks.

"I'm a breast cancer survivor, and I want to produce a line of clothes for women who have had mastectomies and don't want or can't have reconstruction and just want to be flat." My spiel was well rehearsed by now.

Dead silence. Gabrielle, her femininity oozing, looked at me blankly.

"Why do you want to design *zeez* clothes?" she asked in her carefully preserved French accent. "I don't understand. Why would you not want zee breasts?"

Then, after a moment, she said, "Okay, . . ." and flapped her hands against her hips. "Whatever you want." She would do this, but with her own French attitude.

She clearly thought, "Why in the world would I *not* want breasts? Having these spectacular objects is part of being a woman." Gabrielle's world was a showcase for her femininity. Her femininity was her power. She knew how to navigate our misogynistic culture and couldn't comprehend why anyone would do otherwise. And why would anyone want to wear loose clothes? My drab body looked ridiculous next to her form-fitting bright pink knit top and equally bright green pants.

But, in my mind, my choices were clear. I consciously chose to not have breasts. My rejection of my implant and fears of future problems had given me what I felt was no choice. I was breastless. I could choose whether to wear a prosthetic or not. My strength was in my mind, not my body. I did not need breasts.

I took control. "Why don't we start by making a basic pattern?"

"Whatever you wish."

I handed her a tape measure and removed my blouse to have her take measurements. *Keep up the front,* I told myself. *Stay in control.* I'd had a safe life until now, hiding my damaged torso under baggy sweatshirts, overalls, and potato sack dresses, but to make this obsession of mine work, it was necessary for me to expose my scars.

"My measurements are important," I said in an authoritative way, "because after a mastectomy, your body is different from someone who just has small breasts. More body mass has been taken away, so the proportion of the back to front is different than a normal pattern."

Wow, that sounded good.

"Okay." Her face was carefully expressionless. I had her take precise measurements of my chest, up and down, around and through. If I had to do this, I might as well do it right and get it over with. The patterns had to fit me perfectly, since I would be the guinea pig for the line.

A week later, she had the pattern and first muslin ready for fitting. This time I went to her house. She lived in an area of small cottage-like homes. The Cadillac, which was proportionally too large for the row of white cottages, was parked along the street. Her front yard was landscaped with a few flowering plants. I knocked instead of trying the old-fashioned doorbell, and a dog went into a barking frenzy. Gabrielle came to the door holding a small black poodle, which was still barking.

"Hellooooo. Come in."

Mahogany paneling, which looked like the house's original woodwork, lined the walls. Knickknacks, china teacups, porcelain figurines, and small paintings filled the rooms. It was a lovely home. It fit her. Everything was delicate. The house and her stuff had definitely seen better days, but you could tell that everything in the house was important to her, representing years of collecting with her now-deceased husband and reminders of her children and grandchildren.

She led me into a small sunroom, where she proudly showed me the area she had set aside for our projects. This was a promising sign. I just hoped she was good.

She was. We created our first masterpieces.

My first disciple, Nina, was a friend who'd had a single mastectomy. One aspect of my designs was to enable single-mastectomy women to shun prostheses. I had watched her fumble with her migrating prosthesis, discreetly trying to shove it back into place. Who would not want to throw away that plastic, anatomically correct weighted blob?

Nina had been intrigued by my line. "It's beautiful!" She was always so enthusiastic. My first creation would go to her.

I was not ready to use my precious bamboo fabric but instead found a gorgeous coral knit. From a slightly scooped banded neckline, strategically placed folds of fabric draped down to hide the fact that she was lopsided.

"Love it, love it, love it!" Nina raved as she twirled around, admiring herself in the mirror.

"Why don't you take it home, wear it, and see how you feel." I was beaming.

"I'd love to!" There was no hesitation in her voice. She felt good.

"Please let me know how you wear it and how you feel. That will help me a lot."

I would learn from her.

At first she was uncomfortable wearing it in public without a prosthesis, but gradually she became more comfortable, and I could see her transformation before my eyes.

My mission took hold of me.

Gabrielle and I continued to work well together. This was not a full-time obsession for her, so I kept my eyes open for another sewer to add to the team, now using an abbreviated spiel: "Hi, my name is Lynne Hanson, and I'm creating a clothing line for breast cancer survivors who have chosen not to wear or can't wear a prosthesis or have an implant."

I was usually greeted with silence or a quick response that told me they were not listening: "We can do anything you want. Just trust us."

Next.

It was a tough sell to explain what my goal was and what fit I needed. How could they understand? After all, they had not undergone a mastectomy, lived flat-chested, and performed a mastectomy on a dress form to discover the massive changes to the body's shape.

Through the Internet, I found Vanessa. I enjoyed listening to her strong Chilean accent, the roll of her r's. I guessed her to be in her thirties. She owned a company with her husband, located just outside Salt Lake City, where Karren lived. Perfect. Another reason to visit Karren.

I sent Vanessa and her husband detailed designs, precise measurements, and my mission statement. At first, as with Gabrielle, I felt the hesitation regarding the basic premise. They followed the usual M.O., starting with "What is she thinking?" followed by, "Oh, that's not a bad idea." Vanessa seemed to get a handle on what I wanted and was willing to work at a reasonable price. My team—Gabrielle and Vanessa—and I were in action.

Kelley and Chelsea's graduations were coming up, and coinciding with that, Gail's daughter was getting married in Kentucky. This trip would be the perfect opportunity to debut my designs. For months we worked as a well-oiled machine, with Gabrielle and I alternating trips from her house to mine, and overnight Fed Ex packages traveling back and forth to Vanessa, filled with fabrics, drawings, and garments. I gave the more complicated designs to Vanessa, and to Gabrielle, I gave the designs where fitting me was key.

While we were working in my studio one day, Gabrielle clearly had something on her mind. She peered over her brightly colored reading glasses.

"May I ask you to explain something?"

Oh boy, here it comes.

I was expecting, "Why would you not want breasts? Is that not the basis of our femininity?" I was formulating the answer in my mind. I would politely tell her that we could have our femininity without breasts. That this line of clothes would help us feel feminine.

"All of your designs use such drab colors, but your art is so colorful. Why is that?"

Not the question I was expecting.

She was right. My artwork surrounded us with color. The studio itself was vibrant, with the bright coral rug, the red hutch, and the deep red silk curtains framing the picture window. She would not understand that women like me did not want to stick out. We wanted to draw attention away from our bodies. The concept of the line was to confuse and blur the eye away from the chest area, not draw attention to it.

"My art and clothing are two different things. I'm blurring the body with my clothes. My art is an expression of joy." I was trembling inside. That was a plausible enough answer, I thought.

Gabrielle shrugged her shoulders, adjusted her glasses, and continued working.

Her question did get me thinking about the dichotomies in my life, as well as why I had spent so much time and energy changing my name, looking for a new persona. My name, my persona—both were something I could control. What I could not control was having breasts without jeopardizing my health. That was something I couldn't risk.

THIRTY

Annie's Debut

Gabrielle and I had created a few perfect hand-crafted pieces of clothing I could wear. With my limited funds, it was not feasible for me to manufacture any garments until I actually had orders, plus I was looking for real world feedback before I was ready to expand.

Life presented me perfect opportunities to debut the line. First, I would attend Chelsea's graduation in the Twin Cities, then Kelley's graduation in DC, and finally, Gail's daughter's wedding in Kentucky.

At Chelsea's graduation, I was the sole attendee from our family, while her boyfriend, Andrew, had gobs of family attending. The pressure was on. I had to be perfect. My clothes had to be perfect.

I was relieved that the weather was cool, and the tops stayed under a jacket. I was comfortable, felt good about myself and proud of what I had done.

"What do you do in Colorado?" was the question of the weekend.

"I'm designing a clothing line for breast cancer survivors." I felt comfortable leaving it at that. Their polite stares indicated that they seemed comfortable with that too. I wanted to impress Andrew's family, not scare them off with my tyrannical dissertations on why women should consider not having breasts.

Kelley's graduation was next. When I arrived at her new home, she seemed happier and healthier than I had ever seen her. Her eyes glowed, and her tiny nose wrinkled as she smiled broadly.

"Close your eyes and hold out your hands," she said. Her entire body was wiggling, but with precision, she gently placed a long object in my outstretched hands.

She had given me one of the most valuable presents I have ever received—a handheld fan. It was a beautiful blue old-fashioned accordion fan that she had picked out at the National Gallery's gift shop (they have the best gift shop!). Perfect. It was May, in DC, which is notorious for its humidity and heat. I would be a sophisticated woman, fanning herself, and this fan would keep me from passing out.

Luckily, it was unseasonably cool. The graduation ceremony went smoothly, and Kelley and I enjoyed our time together. For the most part, my tops stayed tucked away under a jacket or sweater, which was just fine with me. I was proud of my designs, but not so proud of the body that was wearing them.

During my visit, Kelley and I were shopping at Nordstrom when a saleswoman stopped us. I was wearing one of my sleeveless tops, a beautiful yet subtle copper cotton lace fabric draped gently over a copper cotton shell.

"That's a beautiful top."

"It's her design," Kelley put her arms on my shoulders and pushed me toward the woman.

"I design a line of clothes for breast cancer survivors, and this is one of the designs." I was beaming.

"Oh my gosh," she continued, "my mother just had a mastectomy!"

Another sign!

I went into my spiel. She was intrigued.

"What do you charge for a top like that? Do you have a card?"

I handed over my card, but price? I had not gotten that far. *Think quickly.*

"It wholesales for about eighty dollars." Sounded good.

"Fair price," she noted. "I'll give this card to my mother. Thanks."

Nordstrom, the heart of fashion-conscious America, loving my clothes!

Not one to keep my triumphs to myself, I spent hours on the phone with every friend and relative. I had nothing to sell the woman or her mother, so I hoped that she would not call (she did not), but this was the validation I was looking for.

You would think I had won the Nobel Peace Prize. To me, I had.

Last stop on the agenda was Kentucky, an outdoor wedding—hot, humid, with a chance of pending tornados. And on the wedding day, we also would be busy setting up. I imagined myself with ribbons of sweat pouring down my face (maybe people would mistake them for tears of happiness) and enormous round stains under my arms. But somehow I managed to not ruin the clothes during the setup.

My ensemble for the wedding was the epitome of everything I wanted to convey. A pleated chiffon top with strategically placed detailing took your eye away from the breasts and up toward the face. This was layered over a pleated camisole, mixing fabrics and pattern. A coordinating skirt took it to perfection. I danced the night away, confident that I had a great concept, great designs, and a great team. Annie Flats was here to give women the opportunity to "just be flat."

Soon I would be on to my next challenge. Chelsea and I were attending her childhood friend's wedding in Seattle. I wanted to push my designs harder, but sometimes I push too hard. Hence, the wallpaper dress was born.

Some of the clothing choices I've made are especially embarrassing considering I am a clothing designer. I am either boring or way out there. This was one of my way out choices. The fabric was flowing and slightly sheer—and it called to me. A large geometric art deco print with shades of bluish purple and dull orange covered the fabric. It was pretty and would have looked grand on someone's wall, just not on my body.

But I loved it. I designed a simple short dress and put another dress over that. The underdress peeked out at the neck and the hem. It had pleats to give the illusion of breasts, while the wallpaper fabric skimmed over the body.

Here is the kicker: The underdress was chartreuse.

"Um. . . . . okay," Gabrielle winced. She expected weird designs from me, but this was over the top. Maybe so. I found a blue to match the color in the pattern, and Gabrielle made two underdresses, just to be on the safe side.

When she was finished, she cocked her head to one side, looking at the dresses. "The chartreuse actually looks good."

The wedding was a sea of tasteful neutrals. Even with the blue underdress, I stood out like a sore thumb, but I held my head high. Nothing I could do about it but hope our hosts would someday talk to me after I ruined their wedding photos. I never wore the wallpaper dress again, but I still get use out of the blue underdress. Not so much the chartreuse.

THIRTY-ONE

Annie Goes to Bloomingdale's

I could not shut up or stop working. I had verbal diarrhea of epic proportions with anyone who would or would not listen. Jann was wearing out.

"Today I'm working on the fifth version of the third incarnation of the eighth design," I would report when I made my daily "still alive" call.

"Mm hmm."

And when she managed to escape me, I'd call Karren, then Kelley . . . and on to Chelsea.

We were moving along, but now I needed an infusion of capital to make it a success. There are a zillion great designs and ideas, but the successful ones are backed up by investments. I decided to team up with a store that had production and advertising capabilities. They would line up for this opportunity, I thought. I envisioned racks of clothes, my logo in lights, and me on Oprah—again (because we'll have become best friends by then, of course).

I targeted a dozen chains with the right image and manufacturing capabilities, such as Bloomingdale's, Ann Taylor, and Liz Claiborne. I needed to go with larger companies, not boutiques, so that they would have the infrastructure to manufacture their own garments. This way there would be no ginormous financial commitment for manufacturing from me, plus, the company would be invested in the line's success. Brilliant, eh?

Of course I thought of Nordstrom, but it was headquartered in Seattle, and I had planned a trip to DC. Chelsea and Andrew had recently moved to DC, and now I could visit both girls at the same time. I would start with companies on the east coast. Nordies would have to wait.

I formulated a professional yet heart-felt letter and sent one to the top official in each company. My idea was out in the world, on its own, ready for the taking.

After one week, three days, and eight-and-a-half hours (but who's counting?), I received my first response—an email from the president of Bloomingdale's. Bloomingdale's! The president! He wanted me to meet with the vice president of fashion. The vice president of fashion!

I was on the phone again, calling friends, family, and probably some foes. Two days later I received an email from the vice president. I tried to convince myself that I would be happy just to get through the meetings without making a sweating, bumbling fool of myself, but I wanted a deal. I wanted a deal more than anything in the world. I would have sold my soul for a deal.

I flew to DC and took a non-Vamoose bus to New York. I missed the driver, John (and my corned beef sandwich), but I didn't miss the drama of my earlier trip.

It was the week before the 2008 presidential election. The air in both DC and New York City was electric with anticipation. I stayed with Ty in Brooklyn my first night and woke up wanting the day to pass quickly. My meeting was the following day, and there was nothing more for me to do but wait.

"Let's watch *Gossip Girl*," Ty suggested. His voice and facial expressions were always just this side of exaggerated, giving the impression that he was really excited about whatever he was saying. But that was just Ty. Life was a stage.

"What's *Gossip Girl*?"

"It's a catty, gossipy show about rich, spoiled teenagers. You'll love it."

We spent the day lying on Ty's bed, watching episode after episode of one of the most mindless shows I have ever seen. It was perfect.

I rehearsed my spiel over and over again and practiced breathing exercises to stay calm and dry. That evening, Ty drove me to the northern end of Manhattan, where I would spend the night and the remainder of the trip with Jeanie, my college roommate from Parsons, the New York design school I attended. She and her husband seemed as excited as I was about the meeting. They were the perfect people to be with.

The next morning, they drove me up to the front door of Bloomingdale's. I was ready. I wore one of my custom-made Annie Flats gray tops, sleek black pants, and a slick leather blazer. My samples were in a black garment bag, and I carried an expensive but simple black leather purse and black leather portfolio. My hands were full, but I was determined to pull this meeting off with style and grace. I was a breastless fashionista.

I was twenty minutes early, so I decided to walk around the sales floor to soak up the atmosphere—and soak up any sweat. I sauntered across the sales floor, with the absolute certainty that this was where my clothing and I belonged. As I was relishing my place in this world, my portfolio slipped out of my arms, plummeted to the ground, and scattered across the floor. Drawings everywhere. *Stay calm.* I picked up the pages, one by one. With as much grace as I could muster, I carried my precious cargo against my chest to a corner of the store and put the portfolio back together. I was not sweating. *Breathe.*

I found the office, where the vice president greeted me politely and showed me into a meeting room. She was older than I thought she would be but looked every bit the part of the New York classic fashionista. In many department store offices, the employees are very young. A buyer can be in her early twenties, so I hadn't known whether I would find a trendy young upstart or a crone from the book *The Devil Wears Prada.* She was neither.

Relieved, I hung up my samples and gave her a copy of my mission statement. I was surprised when she took the time to read it. I removed my blazer to be proactive about the sweat factor, and when she was ready, I spoke slowly and calmly, explaining my concept and each design. The presentation was flawless. She listened intently while taking notes. Notes are a good sign.

She gave thought to what she was about to say.

"What are your production costs?"

My excitement intensified.

"I want to work with an organization that already has production capabilities, so we can keep the production costs down," I answered, hoping that she would volunteer to make Bloomingdale's my vehicle for success.

"We don't manufacture anything."

Okay. . . . we can overcome this. Just give me the orders, and I will find a way.

"Your line is beautiful," she continued. "The concept and idea that you have is commendable, but I don't feel that it's suited for a large store such as ours. It's a very personal product, which needs to be explained by a trained salesperson on a one-to-one, personal level, someone who can take the time to explain the product and concept. I think it would do better in a small boutique."

The meeting lasted an hour and a half, during which I spoke clearly and eloquently, without breaking a sweat. I had not sold the line or the concept, but I had conquered the sweat. Her comments made sense, and I would process them and move forward.

Her favorite design? The wallpaper dress. With the chartreuse underdress.

The remainder of the visit was just for fun. I spent more time with Ty and friends. I was swept up in the joy of the city when it was announced that Obama had won the election. Our new president and I were on our way to saving the world.

154

I heard from the other stores and manufacturers. No interest, but I was not discouraged; all I needed was one break, and it was just a matter of time and perseverance. I had lots of the latter. In high school, I had been a loner, and when it was time to sign yearbooks, I was desperate for someone to sign mine. I asked my art teacher, whom I idolized, to sign it. He scribbled, "To Lynne, who refuses to be ignored."

THIRTY-TWO

Standing Naked
in Front of Class

I was not finding the business partners I hoped for. My twelve complex designs needed to be pared down to six less-costly designs, a more manageable collection and more easily funded.

Ideas flowed, from developing a website, to wholesale sales to specialty stores, to home party distribution, or a combination. Every day I got on the bandwagon of a different way to market, hoping at some point the path would organically appear. As a Chanukah present, Jann and Jack, Kelley's boyfriend, surprised me with a website for Annie Flats.

I sent an email with a link to the website to all my contacts and to anyone who would give me their email address. It would just be a matter of time before the word would get out, and mastectomy survivors everywhere would see the beauty of going flat. It was a grassroots approach. Even though I had a global solution in mind, I took it. It was a first step.

I was up and down, one day committed to the website, and another, coming up with money that I did not have to attend a health industry trade show in North Carolina. The trade show route meant selling to small specialty stores, and I would need a manufacturer who could handle small quantities. Vanessa had a connection with a small manufacturer. Mind you, two hundred pieces was the minimum quantity, which was too many pieces for me to manufacture on my own, but if I had orders in hand, it could work. It was a risk, but if I wanted to succeed, I had to take the chance.

The trade show in North Carolina would be expensive, especially with airfare, but I decided to do it. I designed a booth that was eye-catching, inexpensive, and easy to transport. I purchased inexpensive dress forms to perform mastectomies on. It was going to be a lot of work to perform three, but I was a top-notch surgeon. The forms would show how my designs worked.

I gave Gabrielle and Vanessa new designs to work on. The old designs were excellent, but I needed simpler ones suitable for manufacturing in small quantities. While Vanessa and Gabrielle worked on the garments, and I waited for my surgery patients to arrive, I designed a new logo and hangtag.

A month before the show, I went to visit my mother in San Diego. Karren joined us, and I'd promised to model my new line for them. From there, Karren and I would fly to Salt Lake together, where I'd meet Vanessa for the first time and we'd work together in person on samples for the show. I wanted Karren at that meeting because I valued her opinion. I was also nervous about exposing my body to Vanessa. She had my measurements, so she knew what my body looked like, but only on paper. I kept reminding myself that to succeed, I would have to sacrifice my modesty.

I ordered a sizable quantity of my wonder bamboo fabric, thinking ahead to manufacturing, but when I opened the box, it was the wrong color—cream. Panic. I checked the order slip—black. Clearly, this was not black. How could they get *that* wrong? Vanessa needed the fabric ASAP, but it was Friday afternoon, so the fabric offices were closed. I would have to wait until Monday morning.

Early Monday, a new shipment was on its way. It was the right color, but this time the fabric was flawed—it had holes.

They sent additional yardage to compensate, but the holes were in random places, making the fabric impossible to use for manufacturing. I sent it to Vanessa anyway. She could make the samples, and there would be time after I took the orders to correct the problem. These things happen.

It was D-day: I was about to show the new garments I'd designed and Gabrielle had sewn to Karren and my mother. Although I wanted to believe that the designs were good as my original designs, in the back of my mind I knew better, but I ignored these thoughts and moved forward. The clothes could be refined later. The fabric, even though it was my wonder fabric, had somehow lost life when it became a garment. The clothes were soft, antibacterial, and made of sustainable fabric to boot, but they were drab—even for me—and lifeless. I didn't want to model them, but my mother and Karren were waiting.

It was like those nightmares when you are standing naked in front of your class. Only this was real.

I stood in front of the kitchen table. My mother and Karren forced a smile.

Silence, except for the sound of Mom scraping the bottom of her bowl of fruit with her spoon.

"Well, it's a start." Karren adjusted her taupe glasses, her clear blue eyes still a striking feature behind them. Her hair was now a solid white, short and spiky. "I'm not sure it's exactly what you want."

"It's not your best look," my mother chimed in. She refused to give in to wearing glasses and had deep wrinkles between her eyes from always squinting. Her gray shoulder-length hair was pulled back and fastened with an exotic clip she had found at a garage sale.

"Let's analyze this." Karren pursed her lips in thought. "It has some good ideas, but I think you need to keep working on it."

She always insisted that I push myself beyond my first try and learn from my trials, not expecting every effort to be a winner. It drove me nuts, but unfortunately, this time she was right.

My mother was out of her chair, tucking, pulling, and gathering the garment. She was in her late eighties yet had the agility of a thirty-year-old.

Then I felt hot flashes taking over. I wanted to rip the clothes off and throw myself into baggy sweats, never to come out of them again.

We all knew. It was not coming together. All I heard was chatter, and all I wanted to do was cry.

Karren's eyes softened. "Maybe you should think about not going to the show."

There it was.

"Maybe you should pull out and not rush it. It would be better to lose the deposit than to spend a tremendous amount of money and time to show up with a product you won't be proud of."

She was right. I phoned my rock, Jann, who agreed. "I'm sorry, but they're right. I didn't want to say anything, but they're right. The designs just aren't that great. It would be best to pull out of the show, work hard until they're perfect, and go to the show next year."

It was a heartrending decision, but I canceled. Deep down I had known long before this day, but I needed my support group to give me a dose of reality. I could not do it myself.

I was still scheduled to visit Vanessa to fit the garments she'd been making. It made sense to continue, but now I openly doubted myself. The basic premise of the line was in question. It was not just that the fit was wrong. The fit was wrong because maybe, just maybe, a woman needs breasts to get the right proportions. Was it possible that I needed breasts? My clothes looked like gobs of fabric across my chest. The shape does not undulate in and out, like breasts do. The design does not flow around my body, blending into the side and back.

I had a front and a back, but no depth. I was two-dimensional but needed to be three.

What was happening? Was I a traitor to my own cause?

No. I had to follow through.

Vanessa's studio was in a modern office building near Salt Lake City. I had guessed right about her being in her thirties. She was dressed in a classic but funky style, much hipper than I would have thought for someone living in a small Utah town. This was conservative country, the home of Brigham Young and the Mormon Church. She and her husband had come to the States from Chile, probably through the church. Karren noticed the traditional Mormon underclothes beneath Vanessa's funky outfit. What a dichotomy.

Vanessa and I went into a side office so that I could change into the first top. She seemed excited to see her creations on me.

Here I was, feeling old and insecure, not the trimmest person in the world, about to undress in front of one of the cutest, most fashionable young women I had met in a long time. I had a tank top on under my shirt, but she would clearly see that I was misshapen and flat.

Suck it up. She knew I was flat. It was going to be worth it. I needed to do this so my disciples could proclaim their breastless freedom.

She wasn't fazed by my damaged body. So much for my self-consciousness. But the new garments were snug, and getting in and out of them required her help. I began to sweat from embarrassment, tussling with the clothing, and hot flashes. One thing I can count on is for hot flashes to come at the most inopportune times, and my flashes, also known as power surges, were a work of art. First the sweat—lots of it. So much for my pristinely placed makeup. Then came the red. Not just a flush, but big, bright, Rudolph-the-red-nosed-reindeer red. And not a full-face flush (I can't believe that I would wish for a uniform flush). Imagine your cheek with a neon-red perfect square. Just your cheek. As though you'd applied your entire case of blush in a deliberate square with perfect ninety-degree angles.

I was a sweaty, neon, flat potato trying to squeeze into a tight sack.

Karren, Vanessa's husband, and their assistant sat in chairs placed along the long wall of a rectangular waiting room. I came out and stood at one end.

I was standing in front of everyone, including the spirit of Monica Silverman, whose body Karren's reminded me of. Their bodies were slim, no hips, and clothes just elegantly and effortlessly draped around their bodies. I had a choice at that moment—skulk away or embrace the situation and get over it. It was time to get over it. Monica Silverman was no longer going to control my self-image. My body was not so bad for a fifty-eighty-year-old. I still had a waist, and a flat stomach. What more could anyone ask for? I lifted my chin, took a breath, and began calming down.

Monica Silverman had nothing on me.

Vanessa's husband took notes as I played fit model and we made corrections to the garment. Karren looked on and added her opinions.

"Is it tight here and loose there?" Vanessa and her assistant pulled and tugged. Straight pins held between their lips flew with lightning speed to nip and tuck where needed. Vanessa's thick, wavy hair flipped gracefully from side to side.

"I think the pattern needs to scoop more here." I pointed to places that needed work. We had completely different backgrounds and lives, yet we had fashion and patternmaking in common, and for this moment, we spoke the same language. Comrades.

Yet, I was unhappy with the garments. Or was it the premise?

Karren and I drove to her house in the foothills of the gorgeous Wasatch Range of Utah.

"Where should we eat tonight?"

"I don't know. How about Rio Grande or Barbacoa?"

"Who has the best margarita?"

"Rio Grande."

"Rio Grande it is."

World peace–level problem solved.

Our conversation then ventured back to the clothing line, and that led to body image.

"I've never told anyone," Karren confided. "But as a kid, I never took dance classes because I didn't think my body was feminine enough."

Doesn't every girl want to dance? She had never allowed herself because she did not feel feminine. Wow. She was beautiful. Her body was perfect. I never loved my body, but that never stopped me. I was damaged, but I felt feminine. Go figure.

In the end, this trip had made me feel better about my body, better than I'd felt in decades. But I was not feeling better about Annie Flats. There were cracks in my crusade.

THIRTY-THREE

A Perfect Tee

I was carrying boxes of fabric up the tight stairs from the basement. My now-not-so-wonderful fabric had traveled up and down many times, from studio to storage, storage to studio. It was getting used to the routine.

"Going to try again?" Jann called out wearily as she came in through the kitchen door. She was getting sick of the routine. Even Rowena was bored.

The clothing line had shrunk, down to three pieces at most, and even those I was not happy with. I tried to develop new styles, even sewed them myself. I could not justify putting any more money into this.

"How long did it take you this time?" She groaned as she turned the corner, grabbing a box that had been positioned precariously on top of another box, just about ready to tumble back down the stairs.

"Three days," I muttered. "I'm getting better. I only lasted a day the last time."

"You and that damn clothing line."

Our frustration levels were mounting. I refused to consider the possibility that to get the look of breasts, you need breasts. Periodically, I would box everything up, put away the hateful sewing machine, cart it all downstairs to the basement, and walk away. This was the way I handled frustration. Packing things away. Moving furniture. But it never lasted very long. I

163

would lug it all back up to my studio to try again. My mission had become an unhealthy obsession, but at least I was getting good exercise.

I stayed up late and got up early. Sleep was not in my vocabulary. Neither was cleaning, showering, or socializing. Jann and my walks with Carolyn and Linda were my only outside life. I piled the failed samples on top of each other to make my sewing chair more comfortable. My focus went from sample to sample—redoing cardigans, jackets, and T-shirts. I thought, talked, and did nothing else.

Jann was ready to disown me. I tried, not very successfully, to temper my clothing talk. Her life revolved around *her* new obsession, a ginormous breed of dog called Tibetan mastiffs. Let me tell you, these dogs are huge. And just as independent as her yaks. She loved a challenge. So I made an effort to talk about them to earn points to allow me to talk about my clothes.

My "still alive" calls to Jann got shorter and shorter.

"Which dog escaped today?"

"Today it was Spudgy, but yesterday, Keniky jumped out my car window. With the window almost completely closed."

"Uh huh. I think I need to make the pleats smaller on the latest top. Got to run, bye."

Linda and Carolyn were my captive audiences on our walks.

"I started a new painting yesterday."

"Are you doing horses again?"

"I didn't get that far. I got as far as painting the background, then the canvas ended up in a corner to make room for the sewing machine."

"I thought you put the sewing machine away?"

"I did. But it came upstairs. It missed me."

"So what design are you working on?'

"A version of the cardigan that I worked on a few weeks ago."

"A cardigan would be good. They can be worn year-round."

"Yeah, you're right. Let's stop at the coffee shop. They might have a leftover bagel for Tula."

My life was a routine of fitful nights, walking, working on the patterns, sewing, cussing at the sewing machine, boxing up the fabrics and sewing machine, bringing the boxes downstairs, walking, bringing the boxes upstairs, cussing at the sewing machine, walking, cussing, bringing the boxes downstairs, and finally, at the end of that day, brooding through the long night.

Then the light bulb went on over my head. I would narrow my scope even more and design the holy grail of clothing— the perfect tee—elegant, simple, and flattering. Every woman loves a T-shirt of some sort and mine would be the perfect tee for upscale women. As I carried the boxes of fabric, the sewing machine, and my tools upstairs yet again, it came to me. A T-shirt would be an ideal giveaway item for Bloomingdale's breast cancer awareness promotion. Bloomingdale's had not seen the last of me. Once I had the slightest opening, I was going to muscle my way through it. My crusade would be saved. I was pumped up. I worked feverishly to design my perfect tee. I tore apart shirts with great fits to copy their patterns and draped neckline after neckline, working to create a garment worthy of Bloomingdale's.

I was planning to spend the summer in DC and was determined to send a sample to Bloomingdale's before I left. Imperfect tees were strewn everywhere. I even eliminated walks as I focused entirely on my conquest. Tula was not happy.

The final design was exquisitely simple and elegant. A large cowl neck cascaded down the chest to hide the flatness beneath. The neckline had the perfect amount of fabric and drape. The bodice fit yet it wasn't tight, curving slightly inward at the waist, skimming the body and the top of the hips, not too short and not too long. The sleeves were three-quarter length and hit the arm at the most flattering point. There was just enough of my bamboo fabric to make the final one, and it was perfect.

I revised the hangtag and logo yet again and composed an irresistible letter to Bloomingdale's. Everything was perfect; even my sewing was acceptable. I coddled my baby in pink tissue with a pink bow to symbolize the breast cancer fight.

Then, with a deep breath, I handed the package to the FedEx man.

THIRTY-FOUR

The Real Reveal

Bloomingdale's response came quickly.
Not interested.
Undeterred, I prepared for a summer in DC. When I left the first time to go to college in New York City, I had sworn I would never move back. But much to my surprise, it turns out I loved the capital, plus now both girls and their boyfriends lived there. We had been spread out all over the world, and now we could be together again. It made sense to relocate there, but the thought of moving to DC was daunting, especially considering the hot, humid summers. I was spending the summer there to see how I could handle it.

My perfect tee would get me through.

Once again, I had too many cars. Chelsea had used our Camry while in law school, but after she graduated, it came back to me. I was driving the SUV I had purchased in Montana, and the older SUV had 267,000 miles on it and was in semi-retirement. I decided to drive the Camry to DC for Kelley to use. She flew out to Colorado to keep me company on the long drive. Tula would come with us, and my nephew and his girlfriend would spend the summer at my house to keep Mona company.

"Road trip!"

Alan and I had raised our family on road trips to our favorite mountains and lakes, but this time we were headed east, through uncharted territory. Kelley and I were excited about seeing the new terrain as well as about spending time together.

We sang at the top of our lungs to *I Love You Always Forever* and Ricky Martin, and we held our breath as we drove through treacherous thunderstorms. We stopped at the arch in St. Louis, and I ran up the stairs like Rocky, with Tula at my side. Da da daaaaaaaaa, da da daaaaa.

Right after we arrived, we went to register the Camry in Kelley's name since DC loved to tow away out-of-state cars. The DMV was in Georgetown, which in the sixties had been a conclave of hippie boutiques but was now packed with high-end chain stores.

"I have to get my DC driver's license plus register the car, so this will take a while," Kelley said, rummaging through her purse. "I think I have all the documents I'll need. It's amazing what I can fit in here." At any one time, she had an assortment of bags, purses, and scarves slung across her shoulders.

"The mall has some stores you might like," she said. "Maybe you'll find something for the summer."

"Great idea." I actually liked the chain stores better than the boutiques. There was more anonymity, and I did not feel so guilty when I inevitably returned the item. "Call me when you're done."

I sauntered off to play sophisticated city woman. I was the epitome of style with my meticulously applied makeup and my perfect tee, a fashionable mature woman who fit flawlessly into upscale Georgetown.

The mall had been added to the Georgetown landscape to look like a street scene out of the 1800s. Ornate patinaed grillwork and greenery lined the brick walkways, which opened onto a three-level covered courtyard. Old-fashioned lampposts added light, although it paled in comparison to the rays of sunlight coming through the skylights.

I arched my chest, my beautifully disguised body displayed for all.

Then it happened.

It happened so fast.

I caught my reflection in a window. *Who was that person?*

I moved on to another window, thinking I could get a better look.

I was horrified.

The draped collar made me look like a clown. A misshapen, flat, freakish clown. My fabric had betrayed me and was clinging to the undulating scar tissue, and my chest looked like a lumpy sack of potatoes. The collar accentuated the wide expanse of my breastless chest beneath a sagging, sweaty face that had lost all remnants of the makeup I had meticulously applied.

I was mortified and embarrassed, but even worse than that was what I was thinking.

I want breasts.

I. Want. Breasts.

I wanted to abandon all my principles. I wanted to go under the knife and put foreign objects into my body. I wanted to give up what I had felt to the bottom of my heart was my mission in life. I wanted to abandon all of womankind.

How could I even consider this? It was a betrayal of monumental proportion.

Maybe I was dehydrated. I was hallucinating. If I kept walking, the reflection would change. After all, walking had always been my savior. The heat emanating from my face was unbearable. The sweat seared across it, the fabric clung, and there was nothing I could do but hope that some other window would transform me back to the woman I thought I was.

And what was I thinking? *I want breasts?*

I could not fully admit this blasphemy to myself, let alone to anyone else. I could not stand living with my body, and I could not stand to think what I was thinking. Days went by as I grappled with my thoughts.

Finally, I came clean to my sister.

"Lynne," Jann said gently, "You've given this your all. You

needed to go through this process and figure out what you wanted. You needed to be your obsessed self and come out wherever that took you. Unfortunately, you've realized what you didn't want to hear. You have a noble cause with no market. Not even yourself."

She was right.

THIRTY-FIVE

Aww, It's Your First Bra . . . Again

K elley was next on my confessional list. We sat on their tiny IKEA chairs in the living room. It amazed me that Kelley, five-seven, and Ben, six-eight (not a typo), could gracefully contort themselves to fit perfectly into such small chairs.

"I want breasts. Just like all the other women." I still could not believe what I was saying.

"When I see myself in the mirror, I see a deformed potato." I teared up.

"Mom." Ever so gently, she scooted her chair closer to mine. "I was only ten when you had your first mastectomy. And it was only two years later when you had your second, so I don't remember you with breasts." Her body was uncharacteristically still. No wiggling or tapping. "After your mastectomy and all the trouble it caused you, I could see your discomfort with yourself. We would all be at a party, and I would notice you."

I looked up for a second, my eyes widening, then looked down in embarrassment. After all, I was the parent. I was supposed to be the pillar of strength to my kids. Just like the commercials on TV and the testimonials of daughters who idolize their mother as their role model and see her as the strongest, bravest person ever, who taught them by example to fight for what is right and be strong. "My mother is my hero," I wished my daughters would say. But no, I was an insecure and flat-chested soccer mom. It crushed me.

But then she leaned forward to tuck a stray lock of my hair away from my red face. "To the outside world you looked fine, totally confident. But I could see this . . . awkwardness that told me you were not happy with your body." She put her hand on mine and squeezed. "It's okay that you want to be like everyone else," she said. "It's okay. You're a wonderful, beautiful person. It doesn't matter if you have breasts or not. Whatever you want. What we do want is for you to be happy and healthy. That's all that matters."

This is my beautiful child, I thought. *I'm so damn lucky.*

We reached across the awkward chair arms and gave each other a hug. Tears welled up in my eyes, and she used the sleeve of her blouse to wipe away a stray drop on my cheek. Our eyes met, then we both looked down at our bodies, awkwardly stretched across the chairs, and burst into laughter.

"We need ice cream," I said. I wanted to crawl into a hole and eat fatty, sugary foods. And move furniture. I wanted to be depressed. I wanted to wallow in self-pity.

But that was not what I was going to do. I would return to the land of the bras. And I needed to do it *now.*

Kelley took me to Saks to see her bra fitter, Ellen. Just another mother (Kelley) taking her preteen daughter (that would be me) to her favorite bra fitter for that special first bra. Ellen had fit both my girls and could tell which size and style fit best with just a glance. I reasoned that if anyone could figure out how to fit me, she could.

It did not hurt that she was older than me, probably in her mid-sixties; I did not have to confront the cute little hard-body salesgirl usually found at department stores or the overly compassionate saleswomen at prosthesis stores, where I felt damaged, surrounded by reminders of cancer. I was

172

not going to go back to that. I was going to move forward. I wanted to be like every other woman with breasts and go to the lingerie department of a nice store.

DC's Saks was located in an area known for its upscale shopping, housing such stores as Tiffany, Gucci, and Cartier. Once understatedly elegant, now the area was more about status. Beautiful young ladies, dressed to kill and shop, mixed with the aging intellectuals of the political elite.

The lingerie department, located on the basement floor of Saks, looked like any other department store lingerie area—except that it housed Ellen. She was helping another woman and politely acknowledged us as we entered her department. The customer seemed to be in her fifties, heavily made up and wearing a flowing sheer silk blouse neatly tucked into her skinny white jeans, which accentuated her size 00 body. She was dressed to impress, and she looked as though she had cosmetic surgery bills to match. As she sized me up, taking in my frumpy clothes, she probably wondered what these peons were doing in *her* store and why they were standing near her. In actuality, she probably was not thinking of me at all, but at the time, I felt as though the entire world was focused on me and the fact that I was about to get boobs.

Kelley and I wandered off to look around while we waited. Ellen's customer was clearly going to take as long as she could.

Finally, Ellen approached us with a warm grin on her face, her graying hair neatly tied back.

"I've had a double mastectomy, and I need new breasts," I blurted. Just get it out there. Red was chomping at the bit to take control of my face. Sweat was not far behind.

"What size cup would you like?" she asked, unfazed, in her New York accent. It was a familiar accent that gave me a scant bit of comfort in this excruciatingly uncomfortable situation.

What size would I like off the menu? Something from column A or column B?

With as much pride as I could muster, trying not to shake too much, I said, "I used to be an A or a B cup, so I guess that's what I'll be."

"That sounds like a place to start." Ellen held out her slim arm and waved us into the dressing room while she went on the search for bras.

"Let's start with these," she said as she knocked on the dressing room door. She brought four different styles. "These are all the same size but fit differently." Even though Ellen looked discreetly toward the floor, I kept my tank top on until she left. I was not ready to show Ellen my scars.

Moment of truth. I had not worn a real bra, much less tried one on at Saks, for almost twenty years. Kelley deliberately looked around the room as I removed my tank and tried on my first challenge, a lacy number.

What wonders a bit of lace can do. I was feeling a bit sassy. *Look at me, I am a sexy WOMAN!*

But the cups were big and empty. Kelley's ponytail brushed across her shoulder as she turned to see how it looked.

Silence.

"There's something missing here." I poked at the collapsing cups of the bra.

"No kidding." Kelley rolled her eyes. "Guess you'll have to get boobs."

Guess so.

I could fill those holes. I had acquired expertise at creating breasts while lopsided. My favorite material for breasts in the olden days, shoulder pads, were out of fashion. Rolled-up pantyhose might do, but I wanted real fake boobs, not improvised boobs like I'd used in junior high. I was not going to mess around with this. It was real fake boobs or nothing at all.

I had a plan in place. I had researched online what was available in prostheses. I was not willing to wait for an online order, and there was a specialty bra and prosthesis store near

Saks. I would pick up some cheap boobs there. But my bra would not come from a prosthesis store. *No.* I was going to get my bra from Saks.

I tried on a different style, with pointy tips. The size was the same, but Oh My God. I felt like I had double Ds.

"I've got torpedoes!"

"Wow, Mom, you're stacked."

I continued to wrestle with each new bra-venture while Kelley fidgeted with her shoe strap, dumpster dove in her bottomless purse, and braided her hair in three different ways. It was strange how even the empty bras inhibited movement. Every time I moved my arms, there were breasts in the way. It was like a stack of books was protruding from my chest and my arms could not get around it.

There we stood, Ellen and Kelley watching as I swung my arms from side to side, all the while brushing up against the pointy cones jutting out from my chest. Ellen's delicate head tilted to one side as she stood by the door opening, as if to say, "There's no way I'm entering the room with this crazy lady." I could hear Kelley's peeps as she tried to hold in her squeaks of laughter. When she could not hold it in anymore, shrill gasps for air penetrated the dressing room area. A fifty-eight-year-old mother of two was rediscovering the world of breasts with all the naïveté of a preteen.

I tried on a few more bras, narrowing it down to two. One was demure, with lace trim. It gave me little bumps of breasts. The other one looked hot, a bit too hot for my fledgling boobs. I was not ready for that. I picked the baby bumps.

"It's the new you. And you need to wear the bra now." Kelley was already out the dressing room door. I followed dutifully.

"Mom, come this way, you're headed for the kid's section." She put her hands gently on my shoulders to guide me in the right direction. "You're white as a ghost."

The entire store must have known that this old lady had just bought her first bra. I tried to hold my head high, tried

175

to keep calm and not walk into anyone or anything with my newly launched torpedoes.

I was exhausted, but I caught my breath, and we headed to the specialty store to purchase my new breasts. It was a small, cramped store, filled with bathing suits and no mention of us "special women." I was thankful for the discretion but not excited to see rows of bikinis and young women with perfect bodies milling about. The only salesperson was a twenty-something, thin, blonde girl who behaved as though this were her first job. Clearly she had no idea what she was doing, and clearly she was not the one I wanted to deal with. It seemed like forever before she acknowledged us, and when I explained that all I wanted were the inexpensive prostheses I had seen on their website, she looked at me with a dazed "deer in the headlights" stare. Nothing between those pretty little ears.

"The owner of the store will have to fit you," she said without interest, "and she's out to lunch, and I don't know what time she gets back."

Great. I wanted to get it over with, so all we could do was wait. Wait, wait, wait. We watched young girls buy bikinis. We watched old ladies buy one-piece bathing suits.

Finally the owner appeared. She must have weighed eighty pounds soaking wet. She was definitely going for the "I'll do whatever I have to do to stay young looking" look. Tons of makeup, many hours in the gym, and probably many hours at the plastic surgeon. Just what I needed. She went to help someone else, not in any hurry to help us. Kelley kept her cool, but I was just about at the end of my rope. I wanted to buy my damn boobs and go.

When it was our turn to be honored by the owner's presence, I gave her my usual spiel. This woman had no sense of humor, no emotion, and no interest other than to sell. She had a set routine, and veering from it was not an option.

176

"We don't know what size you'll need until you try them on," she said coldly. "Plus, you need a special bra. We have those."

It did not matter that I had my Saks bag in my hand, a small bag, just the size of a bra. It also did not matter that I'd told her I already had a bra and did not need the special bras with the pockets for the new breasts. And it certainly did not help when she said, "Oh, by the way, we carry the brand of bra that you just bought from Saks."

I just wanted my boobs, please.

"Mom, please, try their bra on. Please, just do it." The dark circles under her eyes were starting to show. She was tired, I was tired and emotionally worn out, and I wanted to go home.

Fine. Give me your damn bra.

I was handed a medium-size prosthesis and a bra that looked like the torturous Playtex Living bras for well-endowed women. If there was one thing I was not, it was well endowed. The bra was an armored tank, but I was determined to get through this and tried it on, along with the medium breasts. Wow, was I big! I mean huge! They really got in the way. I could not imagine myself accomplishing anything in my life with these enormous mountains.

And then I heard Kelley's squeal, once again trying to hide her laughter. We would be okay.

I politely asked for the smaller size breast. Reluctantly, the owner brought it. They were not much bigger than the shoulder pads I used to use, and they were twice as expensive, but I needed them now. I needed to experience breasts *now.* A day, a week, a month from now was not acceptable. And I could not wear one of those special bras. I needed a beautiful, feminine bra.

Oh, and by the way, after doing a little research, I have discovered that the best price for fake boobs is at Walgreens. com. You got it, Walgreens, the drug store, has prostheses online. Who would have thought?

THIRTY-SIX

Do You Think I Need to Wear Boobs with This Dress?

My new breasts were mosquito bites, but they felt like mountains. Every time I moved my arms, my "huge" boobs got in the way. My daughters watched me with puzzlement as I clumsily maneuvered my way around my breasts.

I realized that I had to face the boyfriends, who knew I was flat. My brain told me that they really could not care less about my vacillating positions on breasts. I was their girlfriends' mother, so staring at my chest was the last thing on their minds. But I was embarrassed. All they had heard from me since we met was how committed I was to this cause. Now all of sudden, poof! I was done with that?

How would I face them with torpedoes suddenly in their faces? Would I proclaim my new body parts and get the awkwardness over in one fell swoop? Or go about my business, not saying a word, yet knowing that my daughters have told their boyfriends that Mom has boobs.

I was familiar with awkward stares from men and women and chuckled when it was clear that someone was trying not to look at my flat chest. They would look into my eyes only to have human nature bully their eye muscles into looking down.

My first outing with my new breasts was under a baggy shirt. With trepidation and the Himalayas sitting boldly on my chest, I marched down the stairs.

Jack was sitting at the dining room table, working on his computer.

"I have breasts."

"That's nice; you look great," he said nonchalantly as he lifted his head, eyes still focused on his computer. There was not the slightest notion of interest in my new breasts.

The glow from my fluorescent cheeks must have been brighter than his computer screen. I took a deep breath, felt a little embarrassed about my narcissistic moment, and headed back up the stairs.

Then it was Andrew's turn. I had already come clean to Chelsea.

"Mom, we love you no matter what your body looks like." The red curls she'd had as a child had been straightened and cut into a sophisticated, chin-length auburn bob. She did not talk much, but when she did, it was powerful. "You know that whatever you decide, we will back you and love you."

There was always comfort in hugging Chelsea.

Chelsea and Andrew had invited us over for dinner. Fortunately, I was bringing Tula, whom they both loved, so the attention was on her as I marched nervously into the apartment.

"I have breasts."

"Uh huh."

It was now on to the real world, beyond the safety of lingerie departments and family. Over the years, Birdie, my Bozeman garage sale buddy/DC friend, and I had become close. We always saw each other when both of us were in DC, which was becoming more and more often, and when not in town, we spent hours updating each other by phone. She was in town and had invited me to the theater, which would be a proper first outing for my new breasts. I chose a loose fitting blouse that I was comfortable wearing without boobs and carefully positioned the bra and prostheses into place.

As I awkwardly maneuvered into the passenger seat, I was concerned that the bra or the prostheses would move around. Just what I needed on my first night out—my bra twisting sideways, or the enormous (in my mind only) prosthetic boobs popping out, with me unable to catch them. But I managed to get in the car and buckled up without incident.

We had barely moved twenty-five feet before I proclaimed, yet again:

"Look, I have boobs!"

She was driving through city traffic and kept her eyes on the road, even though I could see I had taken her by surprise. She could always keep her cool, so I wasn't sure if she was processing what I had said or if she was just paying attention to traffic. After a moment or so, she answered, her tone an odd mix of proud and confused: "So do I."

Maybe this would not be so hard after all.

I spent most of the summer experimenting with wearing a bra and not wearing one.

"Do you think I need to wear boobs with this dress?"

Kelley would roll her eyes. "Yes, Mom. No, Mom. Either way, Mom." Not a day went by when that question was not asked.

At first the prostheses mainly stayed on the shelf. I was too self-conscious about my torpedoes. I felt like they said, look at me! Fake breasts! I was also worried that they would pop out of my shirt if I moved too quickly or twisted in the wrong way, or that they'd slowly creep up my bra to peek out of my shirt.

I wished I still had my implant. Memories flickered of how great I looked after such a long ordeal of reconstruction, only to lose what I had fought so hard for. Then I had flashbacks of the pain, depression, aches and pains that plagued me during that time. They confirmed I'd rightfully made the healthy but painful choice to remove my breasts, but it was a double-edged sword. Boobs gone and health restored. It was worth it.

And at least my fake boobs would not deflate, another constant worry that I had. I wondered how many women got flats. When I had my implant, I would think about what type of impact it would take to deflate the pouch. It had been under my muscle tissue, which definitely protected it, but after all, they were just plastic bags filled with saline solution in them, so something could conceivably pop them, as in the episode of *Will and Grace* when Grace's water-enhanced bra burst. There I'd be, just like Grace, with water spurting from my breast.

But it was moot, after all. Implants were not an option for me. My body had stated loud and clear that they were unacceptable.

For almost 20 years I had been as flat as a board, and that was where I was most comfortable. I went on a few first dates from the Internet, and each time, I chose to *not* be flat. I think I just wanted to be comfortable in a stressful environment, but maybe it was a litmus test. A man who liked me flat chested was a man who wanted to get to know me, not my body.

Come on now, really, Lynne. The dates I found seemed to just want a woman to be by their side and willing to take care of them. I doubt that breasts were the first, or even the last, things on their minds. Anyway, by my age even the best breasts are headed south and not very pretty. The thought of senior sex does not conjure up visions of hard bodies.

I still wanted to hide under my baggy shirts, but as my confidence increased, the clothes became more fitted. Living in the city helped. In Colorado I could get away with wearing the baggiest shirt I could find. I spent my life in a messy art studio, at the grocery store, walking, or on my sister's ranch. Who cared what I wore? Not the yaks or the mastiffs.

But I do like the way I feel when dressed in clothes that make me look as good as I can. I feel better about myself, and I think I project that. As unfair as it is, people treat you differently depending on how you are dressed. I am also continuing to realize that this body is not so bad, especially for my age. My waist is smallish, my tummy is still flat, and now with my new optional body addition, my waist is shapelier, my tummy looks flatter.

Karren used to give me a hard time for always changing the cabinet pulls in the houses I lived in. I could practically hear her roll her eyes over the phone as she sarcastically agreed that yes, tiny little cabinet pulls made a drastic difference in a huge room. In my mind they did, and in my mind, these tiny little bags of polyester fiberfill made a huge difference on me. It's all in the details.

My body is no longer two-dimensional. No longer just flat and wide. No longer just up and down. Now it is three-dimensional. Up, down, and out. It is amazing to me. Even my mosquito bites make a difference. The question now is whether these mosquito bites make enough of a difference to put up with the discomfort that I find from prosthetics. I don't know. I guess time will tell.

THIRTY-SEVEN

Mom, You're Migrating

My minimalist summer wardrobe left much to be desired, especially now that my perfect tee was in the trash and I had breasts.

Kelley and I went to Loehmann's, a now-defunct discount store where you could find designer clothes at discount prices. I had my bra from Saks, and I had added a comfortable sports bra, but I wanted more bras. More bras meant more normalcy.

We waited in line for a private dressing room, but the wait was long, it was hot, and I was dreading trying on bras. I began eyeing Loehmann's communal dressing room, which filled me with an entirely different kind of dread.

Kelley looked at me compassionately. "We'll do whatever you want," she said gently.

"Let's just do it," I said. "I'm hot and tired. Let's get it over with."

It was midday on a Thursday, so I was hoping the room would be empty, but there was a twenty-something girl in there, trying on dresses. She was of average height and not stocky but far from thin. She obviously worked hard to achieve her look, with lots of makeup and a mass of blonde-streaked waves.

The thought of exposing myself in front of anyone, much less this young lady, who clearly cared about appearance, was daunting. I hesitated. Finally I decided there was no room for modesty after giving birth to two children and having two mastectomies, going through reconstruction hell, and surviving more surgeries.

I could and would conquer the communal dressing room.

The room was about ten by twelve feet, and the girl had positioned herself about three-quarters of the way down the twelve-foot side. Mirrored walls surrounded us, and a continuous narrow bench encircled the room, attached to the wall. A few hooks to hang your garments on were randomly placed, which made positioning yourself a tough task. Kelley carefully hung her selection of blouses across from the girl, and I plopped my bras on the bench.

We exchanged glances with the girl and nodded at the dress she was trying on.

"My ex-fiancé is getting married," she explained. "I'm on my lunch break and don't have much time. I need a killer dress for the wedding."

It is amazing what you learn about a stranger in a short amount of time. Understandably, she needed to look hot, which this dress did, but it was so tight on her voluptuous figure that it made her look desperate.

Kelley leaned in and whispered to me, "You're beautiful." She must have picked up on my anxiety.

As one quickly removes a Band-Aid to avoid the pain, I tried to strip out of my sports bra in one smooth movement. My breasts popped out from my bra and flew everywhere, escaping with lightning speed, as if they had been waiting for the opportune time to bolt for freedom. I was facing the wall, and as I fumbled for them, I only got clumsier. Fugitive boobs fell on the floor and bounced around like fleas. The harder I tried to peel the sports bra off, the more my arms and the elastic band of fabric entwined in a tangled web.

The poor girl trying on cocktail dresses may not have even noticed the comedy of errors behind her. She was busy cramming her curvy self into a forest green number that would have made a stick figure look fat. The hem cut her legs off at the worst possible spot, and her arms puffed out of the armholes like marshmallows. She was lost in her own nightmare.

Any shred of self-esteem I had was gone. Kelley was trying on her newfound treasures, but she had not missed a moment. She and I locked eyes and chuckled as quietly as possible. But Kelley does not do quiet.

With as much grace as I could muster, I gathered the fugitives and slipped them into the sexy black number I was trying on. But now I needed to take that bra off and try another. I refused to traumatize that poor girl any more than she already was by exposing her to my body scars. This meant grasping the breasts with one hand while removing the bra and putting a new one on with the other.

The next one clasped in front. Of course it did. I had finally mastered the back closure and now I was facing a new challenge. It is amazing how much you forget and how hard it is to master the technique of smoothly hooking and unhooking bras. Pity the poor teenage boy learning this art form with his first girlfriend.

I tried to study the mechanism, but I had not brought my glasses, so it was all a blur. Kelley was off in her own world, trying on the latest fashions, and our dressing room friend was trying on a bright yellow dress. Clearly this woman needed advice on how to make a man sorry he lost her.

I managed to get the front closure open and put my arms into the straps, but my breasts were nowhere to be found. They had again made their escape and were heading for the hills. Or maybe they were the hills.

My face was beet red, and sweat was on its way. I decided to put the bra on and then try to find my wandering breasts. I figured that since I had mastered opening the closure, it could not be hard to close it. This would be a snap.

Semi-blind, nerves frayed, sweat pouring, hands trembling, I found the closure impossible to negotiate. My face was now the color of the girl's current red dress calamity.

I summoned Kelley.

"I can't get it either," she mumbled, trying to keep her voice down, which, with Kelley's projection voice, is not possible. We were trying to hold back the giggles, unsuccessfully. I am sure our dressing room companion heard us—how could she not have heard Kelley's squeaks? But she ignored our antics, and I was too flustered to care.

We finally got the stupid bra closed. I found my breasts on the floor, under some clothes, and slipped them into the bra.

"You need to pull the back of the bra down like this." Kelley tugged it into place. *Thanks, Mom.* Here I am, an accomplished mother of two grown children, unable to put on her own bra. The girl looked over and commented that it looked nice. She must have thought Kelley had a very "challenged" mother.

Three more bras to try on. I was getting more confident and decided that I had humiliated myself to the point that it did not matter what I did or what I exposed or did not expose. I slipped bras on and off and mastered the front closure. The breasts fell in, out, on the floor, on the bench, and I let them go. They wanted to have a mind of their own, and I gave it to them. As with children, you have to let them go in order to keep them.

The three of us, five if you include my wayward breasts, chose a bra. Not the front closure, thank goodness. Our unanimous choice was black, with lace around the top—beautiful and feminine without being overly sexy. I was ready to push myself. I would try on some tops, but I put my sports bra back on for comfort.

"Try these on." Kelley held out the tops she had picked for herself.

I laughed. "Right. Like those are going to fit me."

"Just for style, Mom. So you'll know what shapes look good on you."

She helped me struggle into the clothing.

"Not bad," she whispered. She looked like the cat that ate

the canary. She was proud of me. The tops looked good, if I do say so myself, and they were not as tight as I would have thought. I glanced over at our companion, who was about done. She had become quieter as she'd realized she would not accomplish her mission during this lunch hour.

I was feeling confident, even a bit cocky, when Kelley gave my chest a funny sideways stare.

"Mom," she said calmly and as quietly as she could. "You're migrating."

What in the world did that mean? I looked down to see two lumps sitting in the middle of my chest. My little beasts (not a typo) had migrated toward each other.

The poor girl, desperate and about to admit defeat, was trapped in a communal dressing room with two crazy women, in complete hysterics about who knows what. Kelley's big brown eyes were filled with tears, her mouth opened wide and gasping for air. All that came out were high squeaks.

My breasts had been lonely and decided to meet in the middle. They had been in cahoots to torture me and were getting together to celebrate their victory.

"This is what I had to live with," I whispered to Kelley, who was waving her hands in front of her mouth, still trying to catch her breath. "Now you see why I chose not to have breasts."

This is what I and countless other mastectomy victims have gone through. The breasts have the upper hand. Your choice is to contend with the migrating beasts or Velcro them onto a giant Band-Aid attached to your chest, in either case hoping that they will stay in place. Or you can get one of those ugly Victorianesque torture bras with pockets, hoping they will keep the breasts in place. These were the choices I had consciously and bravely given up more than seventeen years ago. And here I was, back at the beginning. Times had not changed, but I had. I had gone to the mountain and back, feeling like a conqueror and a failure.

Who knows which direction I will take. The clothing line is officially on hold. I am anxious to get back to my art. I do not want to date, but I do want to feel better about my body, and with breasts, I do. Maybe I *will* get implants. Prostheses are for the birds. But I am terrified of putting something foreign in my body again. What if my body rejects it like it did before? Even worse, what if the symptoms are again so vague that I do not notice my body trying to reject the implants? What if the doctor does a lousy job? Am I up to having surgery every ten years to replace the implants, as doctors recommend? Can I afford the surgery?

I have researched the latest advances in implants, and not a whole lot has changed. A few new products are on the market, but I cannot help being suspicious. My implant had been the latest product, and as soon as I'd finished the painful eight-month reconstruction, the medical community had issued a safety warning for that implant. Would the worry gnaw away at me?

Implants put in under the breast muscle look more natural than those put on top. The problem is that under the muscle requires a more complicated invasive surgery and has the potential to leak into the inner body. On top of the body is a simple surgery, relatively inexpensive, easy to monitor and replace. But to me they look like two half melons stuck on top of your chest. Which is basically what they are.

My chest is riddled with zippers and scar tissue. Why would I want to try implants again, to expose my mind and body to potential trauma? But I want to look good again, and I don't know what to do. Maybe you were expecting that I'd find the answers by now. Maybe *I* was expecting that too.

THIRTY-EIGHT

Full Circle

September 11, 2009. I was back in my house in Colorado, sitting on the overstuffed poppy chair Alan bought for me, my pink "hamster" shirt wrapped around me, waiting anxiously to hear if my Bozeman house had sold.

I had never thought I'd sell that house. It was where my family had started a new life after the post-9/11 economic collapse. It was the house where my husband had died, and where Kelley, Chelsea, Ty, and I had altered and rebuilt our lives to fit without Alan. It was the house where I had become an artist, and where my mission to create an alternative for mastectomy survivors had percolated. I loved that house. I will always love that house.

After Alan died, I worked so hard to finish the remodeling and make it a home he would have been proud of. It was hard to rent it to strangers, and each phone call I got about a repair that needed to be made (and there were many) sent me into a depressed stupor. Now it was time to move on and sell the house, to let someone else enjoy it. It belonged with someone who would love it, not a bunch of random people looking for a place to stay. I was not going back to Bozeman to live; it was not for me. Not the me I was now.

It had been rented for two years, and that spring, I'd asked my tenants to move out. This meant no rental income, and if the house did not sell by the end of summer, I would have to rent it again, which I dreaded.

My property manager (actually my mailman and his wife) and realtor, Susan, worked to get the house back to its original beauty after two-and-a-half years of being a rental. The house was listed in mid-June, and I put it out of my mind during my summer in DC.

Close to my self-imposed selling deadline, my real estate agent called. She had an inquiry from a young couple who loved the house but could not afford it. They wanted to know if I would consider a much lower offer.

"Please thank them very much," I told her. "Tell them that I can't consider such a low offer, but that I appreciate their love of the house and might consider something in between." Then I put them out of my mind.

We will call them couple number one.

Couple number one presented another offer. The economy was still in a crisis, and Bozeman, which was always at least two years behind the rest of the country, had a much longer way to go to recovery.

"Let's make this offer work," I told Susan.

"All right, I'll do my best," she said, surprised.

They would love the house, I told myself.

We had almost reached an agreement when Susan called.

"You won't believe this," she said. "Another party is interested in the house. After all this time, you have two offers! You're still in negotiations with couple number one, so you can consider another offer."

Couple number two matched couple number one's offer, plus they would pay cash, with a two-week escrow. Even though couple number two wanted to remodel the house (it was perfect; how could they tear it apart?), were from California (a strike against them in Montana), and had a last name that rhymed with "mutt," I accepted their offer. It was questionable if couple number one could qualify for the house, and, as I tried to convince myself, it was a business deal.

Couple number two scheduled an inspection. Now tell

me, why would anyone expect a house built in 1946 not to have issues? Along with the house's charm come the issues older houses have.

"You're not going to believe this," Susan said. "I don't know who the inspector was, but he reported that the house 'might' have mold and 'might' have asbestos, and couple number two ran. I couldn't believe that they would run without doing further investigation, but it was their choice. What do you want to do?"

It was back to couple number one to see if they were still interested. They were.

I was still in DC, and my mother had come to spend the week for medical tests for one of her many studies. All of us had gone to a family wedding in New York. It had been a stressful week of traveling with family and the typical multigenerational drama. My blood pressure needed a break.

"You're not going to believe this."

Susan and I were getting used to this start in our conversations.

Another couple was making an offer. This was crazy. The market was terrible, and here I was, with three couples interested in my house. Had I priced it too low, or did others finally see what a special house it was?

"Haven't had this much action in years," Susan exclaimed. "Let me see what I can do."

"When this house finally closes," I told Susan, "I'm going to eat ice cream all day long."

It had been a very long week. Jack and I took my mother to the Baltimore airport, and as we were walking through the terminal, Susan called. She had told couple number three that we had multiple offers, and that if they wanted to make an offer, it had better be good. The cell phone reception was lousy, so I lost the connection before she could finish.

I could call Susan back later. I needed to get my mother to the airport gate. At security, I showed the TSA agent the pass I'd gotten to go through with her to security, but he just smirked when he looked at it. He was not about to let me go through. My mother's name had been put on it by mistake, not mine. As Jack and I were running back to the ticket counter, the phone rang again. This time Susan was able to get through to me that the couple had offered full price. Full price! I quickly accepted couple number three's offer, and poor couple number one lost again.

Jack was able to get the ticket agent to give me a new pass with my name on it. We ran back to the same TSA agent, and I shoved the pass in his face, then ran to catch up to my mother, who was just getting through security. On our way out of the airport, Susan called yet again. "We need to sign the papers now!" she said. "This is a deal we can't lose. Can you get to a fax or email?"

Oddly, the airport had no business center for sending and receiving faxes and emails, so Jack and I stopped at a Kinko's on the way home. I quickly received, copied, signed, and faxed acceptance of the full-price offer.

I couldn't believe this. I felt exonerated. The house was worth what I thought it was. Alan would have been proud; I had done a good job. I knew that the couple would find lots of issues with the inspection, but full price gave me lots of wiggle room to negotiate. I could almost taste the ice cream. It seemed too good to be true.

Which, of course, meant that it was.

The next day, Susan called again.

One "you're not going to believe this" later and she'd explained that the wife in couple number three had recently been diagnosed with breast cancer. "Today she was informed she's been accepted into an experimental program in Salt Lake City. Rightfully so, they do not feel that they could handle a new house and the medical treatment at the same time."

My heart went out to them. How random is it that she would be dealing with breast cancer? I wanted to let these strangers know how much I felt for them and how I wanted to help them in any way I could. But all I could do was say how sorry I was and let them go.

"Is couple number one still around?"

"Don't know, but I'll sure find out." I think Susan was having the time of her life.

Was couple number one still around? Much to my surprise, yes. I hoped it was meant to be. The price was not the best, but it could work. I would make it work. I loved this house more than any other I'd had. It embodied who I was, and it was going to be so hard to let it go, but at least it would be in good hands. Sweet couple number one. They had hung in there, and we agreed on the terms.

Next hurdle was the home inspection. We requested a copy of the original inspection report from couple number two.

"The inspector must have had nothing else to do when he did this," Susan reported. "His final report was fifty-seven pages long! I've never seen such a report."

It apparently included such details as "the righthand corner of the left wall on the northeast, which is the corner of the right wall on the north side, has a small one-inch crack in it."

"This is the craziest report I've ever seen," she exclaimed, "No wonder couple number two ran. I hope I never have to deal with that inspector again."

We gave the report to couple number one and anxiously waited. There were no indications that a couple number four was about to appear. I wanted this deal to work.

Couple number one brought their own inspector to the house. No signs of asbestos or mold. At least we were over that hurdle. The house did have some other issues, so now I waited for couple number one to tell me what repairs they wanted.

They asked for reasonable repairs, and I was happy to comply. There was another tense moment when their agent would not accept the wording of the repairs from the plumber, even though the inspector said it was repaired. We were all so frustrated and tense; the sale was about to fall through because of the direction the basement showerhead turned.

But then couple number one accepted the repairs, and it was on to the final escrow.

On Friday, September 11, 2009, at 11:02 A.M., I was back in Colorado, in my poppy chair.

The phone rang. It was Susan. "It's time to have ice cream."

Of all days for it to close—September 11, the start of my journey, triggered by the 9/11 tragedy and Alan losing his job. I sank further into the womb of my poppy chair, gazing out the window at the Rockies. I often saw deer wandering across my yard, and I hoped that I would see one today.

After what seemed like ages, I got up, grabbed a spoon and the carton of ice cream, and returned to my chair.

I sank into it as far as I could.

Tears mixed in with chocolate chip vanilla bean. The house was gone. Alan was gone. Our dream of a simple life in a mountain town was gone. My crusade to liberate women from breasts was gone.

I dialed Jann's number, composing my thoughts.

But then all the words I had planned to say seemed irrelevant. I took a deep breath, closed my eyes, and, with a slight grin, whispered:

"Still alive."

THIRTY-NINE

Thomas Wolfe Had It Wrong, You Can Go Home

S till alive, still wandering, still breastless, and still lost. I
had tried living in Colorado three times, once for a very
brief stint during college, once as a ski bum in Telluride
with Alan, and now this time. It never worked out. I can't figure
out why; it's a beautiful state, filled with friends and family. It
should have worked, but it didn't.

My home became an expensive storage unit as I spent more
and more time visiting the girls in DC or visiting my mother
in San Diego. Finally I took the plunge and moved back to
my hometown. I purchased a small two-bedroom condo in
Washington, D.C., about a quarter of the size of my house,
with no basement.

My thoughts were on the new life ahead of me, not on
the past.

Before I could make the move, I had to do another purge
of my belongings—and of Alan's. Jann came over every day
and we headed down to the basement where mounds of
boxes filled with Alan's belongings were stored. When Alan
died, we hadn't been in our Bozeman house very long. He'd
never had the opportunity to unpack all his gear. I didn't
have the strength to go through all of it when he died, so it
just stayed in the basement. Some clothes, yes, but the vast
portion was his equipment: fishing, fly-tying, backpacking,
mountain climbing, golf, tennis, you name it, he loved his

equipment. Mountains of boxes that I managed to ignore. I moved everything from that Bozeman basement, still in untouched boxes originally packed in Seattle in 2001, to the dark unfinished basement in Colorado.

After more than eight years, my denial was about to come to an end.

It was time. I could no longer cart his presence along with me. Jann and I got into a routine. She would sit on the stepstool by the washing machine while I unpacked a box. I'd start to freak out and cry, seeing the memories of our 32 years together. Jann would calm me down and I'd take a deep breath. I'd lay everything from that box out on the floor and photograph it. Then I would text the photos to Kelley and Chelsea and they would pick out what they wanted me to keep. I created one pile for keeping and taking with me to DC, one pile to donate, and one pile—I wasn't sure what I would do with that pile. Alan's outdoor equipment was too good to give away, but I couldn't sell it to just any stranger.

This went on for weeks until we were finished. I packed the boxes of what we were going to keep and gave much away. The rest needed a home where it would be appreciated and loved. Karren's oldest son had been very close to Alan and loved all the sports that Alan did. *He* would give Alan's belongings the perfect home.

Early one morning, I got in my car and headed west. Stuffed with all of Alan's goodies, the car was packed to the brim. At the exact same time 600 miles away in Salt Lake City, Karren got into her car and headed east. Before noon, we arrived within 20 minutes of each other at a diner just off the I-80 interstate in Rawlins, Wyoming. There we had lunch and a lovely visit, moved all of the goodies from my car to her car, and I headed east and she headed west. As we drove home, we talked on our phones and realized the significance of what we were doing. I was moving on from my life with Alan. We both cried as we drove.

Houses in Montana and Colorado sold, condo in DC purchased, I was off to my new adventure.

I was surprised at the comfort I felt being back in DC, as I had lived in the west my entire adult life and vowed never to return to my hometown. I loved the umbrella of lush trees covering the grass under the tree canopies. I enjoyed the history in every corner of the city.

Jack turned me on to the pedometer on my cell phone.

"I walked nine miles today."

I was so proud, I pushed myself to see how far I could go.

"The buildings are amazing, every single one is different."

Shacks in Georgetown from the days when the enslaved people who built DC lived there. Mansions in Rock Creek Park belonging to ambassadors and senators. Government buildings ranging from the ornate Executive Office Building to sterile block compounds reminiscent of the Soviet era. I loved them all.

Thomas Wolfe had it wrong. You can go home.

FORTY

With No Support from Our Friends

I was at peace with myself. I was at peace with my flat chest. Sure, I was disappointed that my design mission had failed, but I was ready to move on. I became a quiet advocate to friends of friends, listening to their apprehension as to whether have reconstruction or prosthetics.

"I'm going to have the new silicone implant that Dr. XYZ recommends after my radiation and chemo is done."

"Why are you choosing to go that route?" I was always careful not to judge, but to try to broach the possibility of going flat.

"That's what the doctor suggested."

"Wow, it sounds like a lot to undertake after going through chemo and radiation. That alone will be tough."

"Yes."

Sometimes I would gently ask if bypassing reconstruction and going breastless was an option. Inevitably, they would look at me with a totally confused look or there'd be dead silence on the phone. The notion of going flat had never come up before.

As I got to know the women, I sometimes briefly told them of my experience with implants. I always prefaced it with the fact that I had strange allergies and my experience was not the norm. How I wanted to ask them why they were so determined

198

to have breasts, but it was none of my business and a very personal question. I saw my position as being supportive, not stressing them out even more than they already were.

As I listened to others, not once did I hear that their doctor brought up the possibility of going breastless. The closest I ever heard was the option of prosthetics. Back in my years of mastectomies, being flat was not even a blimp on the radar. Even my beloved surgeons never once presented that option. My HMO was so convinced reconstruction was the only option, they allowed me to hire any plastic surgeon that I wanted, even out of network.

It had not been my choice. I had made no choice. I was faced with a situation that I needed to embrace head on and not look back. I tried not to look back, but instead ended up on a roller coaster. It was something that I truly faced alone. No one else had any idea of my situation and feelings. No support group, no family or friend could help. This was my identity, *my* body image, no one else's. I have always felt very alone with this issue. Perhaps there are others like me. I have no idea how many women have opted to go flat, by choice or not.

Even *I* chose the implant option. I never even considered going flat. It was forced on me. I still wish that it had not been my decision and that I still had my perfect breasts. I don't buy that flat is beautiful; our bodies were designed to have breasts. Remember my analysis of the feminine body and its S-curves, which needs three-dimensional symmetry, not two-dimensional breadth.

Please understand that this isn't a pity party. At no point have I felt sorry for myself, but I do wish that our society and professionals had a more open mind to our femininity. It would certainly help a lot of women.

Instagram has helped a little bit, because now I see many women who've gone flat posting on Instagram. But honestly, they seem a bit too zealous for me: Either show your naked scars or get off the bandwagon. Why can't women admit their body insecurities and support each other with compassion, not preaching? Why can't doctors talk to us honestly about options that might not be the norm?

I had hoped that our society's body image would change after 20 years of breast cancer at the forefront of cancer awareness. Obviously not.

Even my mother, who loves me with all her heart, continues to pressure me to have implants, saying it is worth risking my health. She has a strong scientific background and experiences with her own allergies, analyzes her body and what is happening with her ancient implants and her aging process as if she is her own science experiment, yet she is not shy to constantly tell me that I would be more appealing to men if I weren't flat.

"But, Mom, don't you remember that I had a terrible reaction to the implant? Do you really want me to risk that again?"

"It's worth the risk."

This hurts me to the core. I know how much my mother loves me, I don't doubt that for a millisecond, so for her to say this to me, she must believe this with her entire being. Just like so many.

Looks like nothing has changed. It's a shame. At the time that we are pressed with making what is probably one of the most stressful and important decisions in our lives, and certainly not thinking straight, we listen intently to the experts and mull around and research the options presented to us. I know I did, spending endless hours researching and debating lumpectomy vs. treatment vs. mastectomy, interviewing countless surgeons to do my reconstructive surgery.

Wouldn't it be nice if going flat was one of the options from the beginning?

But our society does not give us that option.

My breasts have been damaged. They had been mutilated

and taken from me. Tattooing beautiful images on our breasts may cover the scars on the outside, but we have still lost a part of our body.

Society makes us schizophrenic. Most models that we want to emulate are still stick thin and boobless, yet many a woman truly believes that she must have large boobs to attract men. *Which is it?* Most of us get lost in the middle and just have what we are given, but given a choice, by way of cancer or just our own body image, which would you choose? And why?

My choice is an easy one. Monica Silverman still influences me. I would choose being thin and naturally small. Like that cobbler with holes in his shoes, I am still the clothing designer who could happily live in sweats and baggy clothes, somewhat on the genderless side, perhaps even go back to my beloved overalls.

So why don't I? It's all in the proportions. Thin can go boobless, wide and solid looks out of proportion without breasts.

"I don't understand what the problem is," I hear from naturally flat-chested , pencil-thin women.

"I hear what you're saying [*my go-to response which I picked up in sensitivity classes*], but women who do not have a beautifully svelte figure like you [*flatter them shamelessly, another handy tip from those classes*] become out of whack and aren't balanced. Our Rubenesque figures need compensating ins and outs."

"Oh, no, all you have to do is wear a scarf and you can't tell." I can't tell you how many times I've heard that. There is so much condescending zealousness in their conviction that scarves solve the problems of the world that I just listen and nod. Clearly I haven't gotten through to the women who have said these things to me. My frustration that these women are so hell-bent on *their* solution being *mine* made me stop trying to explain anything.

I know that they are trying to help, but women need to

listen to other women. Small-breasted or flat-chested svelte women do not have the same issues as women who have lost their breasts.

And why do I care?

After decades, I am coming to terms with wearing a bra and not wearing a bra. I have a new comfort level with my surroundings and myself. When I am at home alone, or wearing a sweatshirt on a walk, the prosthetics stay in the drawer.

But when I am out in public, my little fiberfill friends come with me. Most of the time I wear a sports bra with a cheap fiberfill insert. It isn't much but it gives me the confidence that I need with tops that just don't cut it without a bit of boob.

Dating is sporadic and I never get past first or second dates, so the panic of my date discovering the truth about my body isn't a concern.

Here I am, still obsessing, still self-conscious, still storing fake boobs in my closet.

FORTY-ONE

Let's Analyze Breasts . . .

Analyzing boobs has become a common pastime for me. I can usually spot fake boobs in an instant. I don't profess to be a boob expert, but I will offer my observations. I apologize if this is way too much information. Just as many people with eating disorders watch hours of cooking shows, I watch boobs.

Implants often sit higher on the chest than natural boobs do. Ones positioned under the chest muscle are the more natural-looking ones. Going under the muscle is a more invasive procedure, but the result tends to look more natural than implants positioned over the muscle, just under the skin.

When a woman lies down, her fake boobs don't flatten out like a natural breast does; they keep their shape, sitting up on top of the chest like little mountains.

In addition to all the different sizes, there are many different shapes of implants: ball-like, tear drop, expander-drooper ones, soft ones, hard ones, pointy ones.

I don't understand the ball-shaped boobs. There is no question that they are fake; they just look like the stereotypical sexist cantaloupes-as-boobs. I'm reminded of the scene from South Pacific when the soldiers do a show and the men dress as hula dancers with coconuts as breasts. I often see these breasts prominently displayed in skimpy tops with the complete round edge exposed. I don't get it, but I admire their owners' pride and lack of inhibition.

We are designed with a layer of fat and muscle that goes around the side of the body to the back. Our natural breasts make a gradual transition to this area. But with implants, there is usually a definite separation of the breast and side.

As a sidebar, I hate this muscle. It might have something to do with why I seldom wear a prosthesis. A bra, no matter which one I wear, creates a lump and bump that I find uncomfortable and unattractive. My personal hang-up.

Now let's get into natural breast comparisons. Breasts are as unique as our faces. Perhaps that's one reason why they are so important to us. Natural breasts come high, low, pointy, round, wide, narrow—even our nipples and areolas are unique. They are ours alone and to lose them is like losing part of our unique identity.

FORTY-TWO

... and the Clothes
That Go with Them

Let's review my observations of which clothes need boobs
and which don't. Again, only my opinion.

I love the artform of the slinky, breastless, lean S-shape
form of the female body, especially when strutting the runway
of a high fashion show, dressed not in crass clothes but in
hand-made art. Like a snake, the body subtly flows and shifts.

In contrast, there is a balance of the full-figured woman
with large breasts and matching booty. The balance is there,
they can get away with wearing almost anything. Both figure
types work gorgeously.

But what garments work and don't work on us breastless,
non-stick-like figures?

Form-fitting clothes, on me especially, need boobs. If the
garment is form-fitting, and especially if it's knit, my lumps
and bumps of scar tissue and extra skin absolutely need a
breast to cover them up. I cringe at photos of myself when my
top reveals the ugly truth. I'm honestly humiliated.

Why the hell do I let that happen? I ask myself. *Wear a bra,
for god's sake.* But even that doesn't convince me to do so. I just
change my clothes.

One way to get around this is to layer. With enough layers
and ease of the garment, lack of boobs can be camouflaged.
First, I start with a camisole. Depending on the weather, it

might be a moisture-wicking super fabric or cotton tank. Then comes a lightweight tee, either crew-neck or V-neck.

If I didn't layer, I wouldn't be able to wear a tee, as it's knit and very form fitting. I have discovered the subtleties of tees. Lightweight tissue cotton vs. thick organic cotton. Sometimes model, pronounced *moDELL*, the new name for rayon, is added for slinkiness and wicking properties.

Tees are touchy, sensitive creatures, and each one is unique. Price seems to have nothing to do with quality or fit. It just takes experimentation. I hate to admit it, but my collection of tees consists of more misses than hits. Woven linen is my new best friend. I've found tanks, tees and tunics that seem to be the best bet for me at the moment. I've tried wearing a stretchy step-in Genie bra with tees and it just looks silly. Yes, it gets rid of the ripples of skin on my chest, but the tiny mosquito bites just looks silly.

On top of the tee, I might layer another tee or a light cardigan, flannel shirt, or pullover sweater. I like layering. I think that it might have something to do with my confusion about me. Perhaps like my clothes, I consist of many layers.

Dresses used to take up a large portion of my closet, and they still do, but they tend to stay in the closet. My lifestyle of mucking around in plaster and paint and of walking for miles in dense woods just doesn't call for dresses.

Let's talk about dresses and breasts. The majority of my dresses need boobs. I have a lot of gorgeous sheaths that I purchased during my padded Genie bra period. My breasts weren't large, tiny actually, but it gave enough oomph to the dresses to look good. Even now, when I do wear a dress, I wear a bra. Again, the dresses work better when they are made of a woven fabric, but because of the tailoring of a dress, they need boobs. The darting around the chest area to make "pockets" for breasts screams *I need boobs*. Otherwise there are empty pouches that need to be filled. Even my looser dresses need boobs.

"Do you think I need to wear boobs with this dress?" I'd insist that my daughters stop their busy schedules to look.

"It really needs something, Mom."

"It might look better with boobs."

"You can go either way."

"Do what you want, MOMMMMMM."

My obsession with analyzing breasts has given me a new understanding of fashion and individual choices: revealing vs. not revealing, form-fitting vs. loose and baggy. The skinnier the person, it seems the looser the clothes and the better those loose clothes look. Why is that?

One argument is that skinny bodies look proportional even when they're flat. Most are naturally small-breasted and the body makes sense. Skinny bodies tend not to have the ins and outs of a fuller figure. Therefore, not having breasts does not affect the balance of the body.

Once in a while I will see a photo of me. It is always clear in the photos that I am flat, I am wide, and flat and wide just doesn't look good. I feel as wide as I am tall. There is nothing I can do about the wide part, that's just how my bones are put together. Even when I lose weight, I have to buy the same size clothes that I did before because of my wide frame. That's what I'm trying to get across to the very skinny flat-chested women. When you are wide *and* flat, you're dealing with a brick wall rather than a slender beam.

One of my very good friends went through breast cancer and reconstruction. She had a great deal of trouble with her reconstruction, and even after 15 years she is still having trouble with her implants.

One day I finally couldn't help it. "May I ask you a personal question?"

"Sure." Her warm eyes gazed at mine.

"Even with all the problems that you've had with your implants, why are you still determined to have breasts and take the chance with more surgery and implants?"

She cupped her hands around her small breasts, smiled, and tilted her head.

"These make my body balanced."

Click. She was an elite skater, had been in the Olympics and was a very creative artist. She understood the balance that the body needed to perform the intricate dances and athleticism required to reach the level of achievement that she did.

"I need both of these to balance my body." She reached back to her butt with one hand and kept the other hand on her breast.

That's what I said!

"You understand that because you're an artist," I exclaimed.

"Yes, it makes me who I am."

Yes! I understand her completely. But why isn't that important to me?

Or, perhaps, underneath all of this insecurity lies a tremendously *secure* person. Perhaps *my* identity lies in my art and my closeness to family and friends. Not with my body.

In the meantime, my large assortment of bras, prosthetics, and rolled up panty hose pretty much stay in the back of my drawer. They only emerge when I go on a date or the rare special occasions when the outfit that I wear absolutely needs breasts. After all, my exposure is limited to family and the occasional grocery or art supply store.

FORTY-THREE

I *Am* an Artist!

Back to my life in DC.

For the first time in forever, I had the freedom to do just what I wanted. Much to my surprise, I found I wanted to sculpt. It was odd that I wanted to sculpt after I'd pooh-poohed the fine art world for so long. After all, sculpting is fine art at its pinnacle, there is a limited market for it, and it is exceptionally laborious, especially my version, which demands detailed beading. And patience has never been my strong suit.

My beading obsession began when Kelley competed in ice-skating and I designed and beaded her competition dresses. My OCD personality took over after she quit skating.

"Mom, I'm not sure what you'll do with that beaded wooden plate."

"Lynne, what are you doing beading that wooden egg?"

"Is that a plaster *fish* that you're beading?"

"I'm scared that you're going to start beading the walls of our house."

I wanted to bead everything and anything. It's incredibly soothing and meditative. I love to run my hand through the wet plaster as I spread it across the under form before I bead. I get lost in the texture and undulation of the beads. I love to run my hand over the beads and feel their different textures, following the swirls and twists and turns. I love to examine how the light reflects off the different finishes of each bead and how the light varies within each bead.

209

I guess I have to admit it, I *am* an artist. When I write that, there is a sense of relief. Perhaps this is truly me. Perhaps this is my ticket to be the creative one and dress true to myself, which means that I'm truly free to look different.

There is no doubt in my mind that I want to sculpt and I want to bead.

I started with my go-to horses. My beading is paired with plaster, silicone, preserved wood, rebar, and anything else that I can get my hands on. I amused myself with a list of the materials that I can cart home from the hardware store as I pass through the iconic Dupont Circle, a well-known fixture of the Washington landscape. It is the home to protests, dance parties, tight-rope artists, politicos, tourists, hippies, and everything in between, so my presence is unremarkable.

Just to name a few items, my list includes but is not limited to:

A large roll of chicken wire

Four 8-foot-long 1x10-inch planks

13 boxes at a time of panettone cakes (for my daughter's
   pregnancy cravings)

A large Dremel tool kit

Rolls of copper mesh

Various rocks and wood that I find on my walks

12-foot garden stakes

30 x 40-inch foam boards

The wood that I found on my city walks wasn't as fascinating as the wood found in the cottonwood groves on Jann's ranch in the Rockies; those pieces really called to me. Her ranch is located on an old riverbed and the river-weathered cottonwood is gnarled and swirled like no other.

Native American cultures consider cottonwood to be a sacred wood, and I found this was significant to me as well.

Using cottonwood also gave me another excuse to visit my sister. At Jann's ranch, we spend hours tromping through her fields, climbing in and out of the fallen cottonwoods. We use a chain saw to cut off branches and parts of wood that I think would work, collect the pieces ready to transform into sculptures, and make a "nursery" of pieces that need to weather more. We return to her house filthy, legs scratched, and luckily with all our digits still attached.

My eyes do the initial search, but I find myself making many of my choices by touching and following the grain of wood, exploring the form, colors, and textures. A piece of wood speaks to me and tells me what it wants to be.

Most people fill their suitcases with gifts, clothing, toiletries; I fill my suitcases with wood.

As I work, I push myself, sculpting horses from molded silicone, wood, copper mesh, feathers, and anything that I can get my hands and mind around.

Here and there I sell pieces and have been selected to participate in juried shows and galleries around the country. It is enough to keep me going, but not overwhelm me. It amuses me to see which pieces sell first or are most popular. My guesses are always wrong.

FORTY-FOUR

Finding my Soul in Boobs

I was making one of my regular trips to visit Jann in Colorado, and we were scavenging for gnarled and malformed wood for my sculptures.

"I see boobs," I said as much to myself as Jann.

"You see *what*?

"I found boobs!"

Jann ignored me. She is a literal person, and seeing horses in rotted wood was as far as she was willing to be pushed.

"I found boobs! I'm going to make boobs."

"Oh, I thought that you had decided to try again with implants. You scared me." Jann scrambled over dead trees and brush as she laughed.

"Look!" I was so excited. "These are boobs!"

I picked up a piece of wood measuring about 6 x 8 inches. It looked like a kneecap. But I saw a breast. I looked around and saw more. Smooth boobs, gnarly boobs, boobs with holes in the middle.

"Help me, Jann, these are great!"

"You're right, these are terrific pieces, but what are you going to do with all these boobs?"

"I don't know, but they're so cool."

Jann's husband just shook his head when we brought them back to her house. "Every time you see your sister, you come home with some new bizarre creation, project, or strange medium."

True. This would be no exception.

My mind on fire, I packed up a box of boobs and headed back home.

These boobs represented the multiple women whose breasts were taken from them. Pretty boobs, ugly boobs, boobs riddled with cancer. Boobs with holes in them from multiple lumpectomies, mastectomies. Gnarled and rippled breasts.

My first breast sculpture was easy. It just flowed. I was inspired by an ancient Greek sculpture of a female torso and fashioned my sculpture after her. She lacked a head and arms, but that was fine. I was going for an incomplete artifact like we see in a museum or in the ruins of Greece.

"Mom, you're not getting any sleep."

I was happily possessed as my hands, covered in plaster, created and formed my beautiful creature. She told me what she wanted to be, and she emerged from a blob of plaster and a piece of wood. Her stub of a neck tilted ever so slightly as her body leaned just enough.

Her left breast was wood. The piece of wood, larger than just the breast, extended beyond the breast area and smoothly blended into the plaster torso. The wood was smooth, without a lot of variations in the grain of the wood, and it naturally had the shape of a small, firm breast. The rest of the sculpture was completely covered with monochromatic, textured patterns made from tiny seed beads.

As I beaded, I ran my hand over the patterns and textures of the undulations and forms I created. Different sizes and differences in the finish of the beads added to the complexity of the sculpture. The beads were mainly in golds and ochres, with quiet splashes of blues in various patterns. Sometimes the beading would follow the forms, the ins and outs of the torso, but other times, I went against the form, to create more complexity. I kept the beading simpler than usual because her wooden breast was as much a focal point as the beading.

Cancer: This Is Not A Hellenistic Torso was born. As I

213

always thought that my name was boring, I was determined my creation's names would not be. Not on *my* watch! My clothing lines always had great names and my artwork would not be different. She was accepted into a prestigious show in Georgetown and was the first piece of art at the show to sell.

Cancer: My Body Is Not That of a Ballerina, and *Cancer: They Seem To Be Coming Out of Everywhere* followed. I was on a roll with my sculpting, contrasting wood with beading as my statement about breasts. cancer and body image.

Ugly beautiful. My work is ugly beautiful; that is what I am all about.

I am fixated on *ugly beautiful.* Those words are placed prominently on my inspiration board in my color-filled studio/home.

What does that mean?

Chartreuse. My favorite color. Yes, the color chartreuse— it sums up ugly beautiful. It's an undefined color, one that varies in definition by the author. It can range from a clear apple green to a muddy brown sludge. I lean to the brown sludge side. There is a beauty to the ugliness of the color and its complexity, just as there is a beauty to the gnarled wood and the distortion of my art.

"Okayyyyyyyy."

This is the usual response when I mention my art to my family and friends. I have finally identified myself! Is my art a metaphor for me, for my life, for how I see myself? Is it how I see myself and why I can't seem to find my self-image, my changing view of my boobs?

Beautiful, yet distorted and damaged.

At first I wondered if people would accept this work, as they're not the usual tormented artist's statement of the world around them, nor are they beautiful landscapes, serene and optimistic about the world. They've been accepted to galleries and shows, but as of yet, the message has not widely resonated.

In addition, I continue to work on my horses, which sell well, expanding my mediums to paintings, and encaustic wax painting and sculptures. Wax melts into beading, which melts into plaster, which melts into wood.

It reaches my soul.

FORTY-FIVE

Defining Femininity . . . or Not

It's been a tough journey, and I'm certain that I've not reached the conclusion of my soul-searching adventure. To people who haven't dealt with losing a small but defining part of yourself, it's not a big deal.

I admit, I haven't had as much empathy as I should have for skinny people who are distraught over gaining a few pounds. In my mind it's no big deal, but I intellectually realize people with eating disorders might see themselves as fat, no matter how thin they are. It's all in our perception of ourselves. Some women need breasts to feel complete about themselves, maybe even large breasts. Fair enough.

Yet, my blood boiled as I read an advice columnist's idiotic comments about men *obviously* supporting women having a mastectomy or going flat.

Yes, it would be lovely if all men supported and loved their partners whether or not they had breasts. And yes, there are lots of men who do physically desire their beloved whether or not they have breasts.

But many times it *does* matter, subconsciously or not. As much as my husband loved me, he never touched me after my mastectomy—a hurt that still lingers, almost twenty years after he died. Yes, I knew he'd much rather have had me alive without breasts than dead with breasts, but we are creatures of our society and human nature, and to say that it doesn't matter is baloney.

Perhaps I'm so obsessed about my flat chest because I work in visual media and am acutely aware of the distortion of my body. Perhaps it's because I'm a clothes designer and understand the symmetry of the female body. Or perhaps it's just because I'm so insecure about how others perceive my body.

Did you catch that? This is an epiphany of sorts . . . *I'm insecure about how I think others perceive my body.*

Very narcissistic of me, I know. I preach to others that people are too busy worrying about themselves to judge or worry about others, so perhaps I should practice what I preach. After all, most of time I *do* feel confident and feminine with my flat chest. But then *whammo*, I'm suddenly knocked in the gut when I catch a glimpse of my flat self in an unflattering two-dimensional way, or hear something that could be construed as criticism of my appearance. Back to my insecure hole I crawl.

One of my dates casually mentioned that there was nothing sexier than a woman in a white T-shirt and jeans. I liked this guy and wanted to impress him. Then I thought, *but how can I wear a tucked-in white T-shirt without boobs?* I donned my favorite Genie bra, manned the bazookas, found a flattering white T-shirt, tucked it in, and off I went. As I approached my date, I removed my jacket with some Gypsy Rose flair, and va-va-voom! Guns a-blazing! My tiny mosquito-bite pretend boobs felt like they were practically jabbed into my date's face.

As I sat down, I pondered, *Why did I need to do this?* He was impressed, I could tell. Even this wonderful man, whom I knew could love a person with or without breasts, was swayed by my boobs.

So, to get to the main point: What convinces women that their breasts are such a vital part of their femininity that they go to great and uncomfortable lengths—even risking their lives—to keep them or enhance them?

There is no right answer. Everyone is in a different mindset and different circumstance. And everyone has a right to change their minds, just as I have, and to change their minds again and again. As I have.

At what point do breasts tip the scale of femininity? A transgender friend was desperate for her breasts to develop. She couldn't get her hormones legally at the time, so she risked her health and safety by buying illegal hormones that had been smuggled from Mexico. Now she has breasts. Yet, she does not wear anything to draw any sort of attention to those feminine parts. She does not date, she lives a very solitary life, yet, by God, she wants those breasts! Why?

"Why am I keeping these saggy things that just get in my way and make me so uncomfortable?" Countless friends rhetorically ask this about their own natural breasts. Women after reconstruction fight to keep implants that fail and can cause other complications, and have surgeries that take away their muscle strength. Why?

I cannot forget an incident that happened when I was in my overall and cropped-hair phase. I was picking up a pizza and the waiter was turned sideways to me, so he could only see me out of the corner of his eyes.

"What can I help you with, sir?" he asked.

My heart stopped and I realized that the combination of my hair, choice of clothes and flat chest truly did make me look like a man. Would breasts have helped? In my mind, absolutely!

I remember this event vividly, but still, I do nothing.

Well, not *quite* nothing. I prefer gender-neutral and casual clothes like jeans and overalls, but my lack of breasts leads me to think that I need to consciously choose a more feminine look. As a compromise I wear very classic clothes, very simple and clean to avoid bringing attention to my body. *B-o-r-i-n-g*!! So I add an interesting and eye-catching necklace and earrings, and sometimes I add a scarf to bring attention away from my body. Safe.

218

I tell myself that I'm channeling Audrey Hepburn in the movie *Funny Face*—classic bohemian chic and simple. I say my art will speak for me, that I'm just a behind-the-scenes person (then what the hell am I doing writing this book?).

In the end, what makes a woman feminine? Actions, behavior, body type, breasts? Is a natural-born flat-chested woman any *less* feminine?

What are we looking for with our own body image? Why did I, dressed in overalls and with my hair cropped short, feel blindsided and hurt when a waiter mistook me for a boy? What did I expect, or what was I looking for? I'm much more comfortable hiding in baggy clothes, yet I rag on myself for not putting on a bra and playing the game. Nine times out of ten I'm comfortable in my skin, but every once in a while, I find myself regretful that I don't go the extra mile and wear the damn bra.

Recently, my family and I bumped into a nice older man and we all had a good time just chatting. For a moment, I found myself thinking that I could be interested in someone like him.

I felt my nerves get the better of me. Shit. I was ashamed of myself for worrying about a man being turned off by my deformed chest. Angry at myself for judging this stranger to be superficial enough to care if *I* had breasts, but also mad at myself that I chose to not wear breasts yet at the same time allowed myself to become upset about not wearing breasts.

So, let's get to the bottom line here. Do I feel less feminine without boobs? That's a loaded question.

It's not that I feel less feminine, it's that I expect others to see me as less feminine. Yes, I feel feminine. My DNA is feminine and nothing will change that. I feel just as feminine and sometimes more so in sweats vs. an evening gown. My own feelings of femininity have nothing to do with it. It's about my projection of how I think others see me. It's about looking at a photo of myself and only seeing the way the clothes droop and sag from my wide, concave chest. That is how others see me and if the photo is a realistic projection of how I look, I hate it.

This goes against all I know as a clothing designer.

And it looks ugly.

In this new world of social media, I thought that perhaps I could find some answers for my body identity. There are plenty of Instagram accounts of brave women, baring their flat chests and their scars, proclaiming their newfound freedom and self-identity. How happy and proud they seem to be.

I am jealous. Why can't *I* find the peace that they portray? I have a cynical yet Pollyannaish view on life, and I suppose that my view on breastlessness is no exception. These women are so zealous, when I look at them I reflect: *Thou protest too much, methinks. Is your comfort level real?*

If so, how lucky they are to be so comfortable in their own skin. Were they always like this, or did their newfound freedom come with their mastectomies?

I've never been comfortable in my skin, a product of a mother who was obese as a child and developed an eating disorder later in life. Also a product of a loving yet judgmental father who informed me minutes before a date that I really needed to lose some weight.

No, I can't blame this on my parents, I'm old enough to take responsibility for my own actions and feelings. *Get over it*, I constantly tell myself. Nor can I blame the doctors at the time of my mastectomies. True, there was no guidance as to alternatives to reconstruction other than prosthetics. No option to just go flat. But I can't blame them. I certainly could have come up with that option on my own.

Will going flat ever really be popular? Or are we programmed in our female DNA to have breasts, that they're just as important as any limb?

Almost thirty years after my surgeries, I still feel the need to apologetically tell doctors and nurses when they first examine me: *I have to warn you that I've had a double mastectomy and it's not pretty.* I know that they have seen worse, but this is *my* worse and I don't like it.

Is this whole journey of mine just insecurity? Or is it me showing my true strength?

It's such a waste of time to spend our energy worrying about body image, especially when it boils down to what we think *others* think of us, not necessarily what we think of ourselves.

We are all living contradictions.

I know *I* am. I'm most comfortable in baggy clothes, but I have a trained eye and a love of the feminine form.

Preppy yet hippie, overalls with pearls, Audrey Hepburn meets Betsey Johnson.

My art and home are filled with form, color and texture, but my clothes are all black, drab, and neutral.

A penchant for expensive handbags, but nowhere to carry them.

I'm learning and adjusting. I've made my decision. At least for now. I will forgo the breasts unless the clothing I choose to wear dictates that it needs boobs.

I've vented, analyzed, struggled, cried, and laughed. The bottom line is that now I'm going to accept myself.

Flat chest and all.

FORTY-SIX

Resource Guide

V1.0 January 2022

Our individual cancer journeys are complex—simultaneously universal and unique to each of us. We all need different support at different times. I hope this resource guide helps you find the support *you* need—and I'm not just talking about bras!

Scan the QR code below, visit my Amazon.com author page or stop by my website, https://doineedboobs.com/, for the most current version. My publisher promises we'll update the resource guide in the print and eBook versions of *Do I Need Boobs with This Dress* as often as possible.

I'd love to learn about other groups or networks, especially local organizations. Please share with me at lynne@doineedboobs.com.

CLOTHING

Company	Website
Athleta	https://athleta.gap.com/?ssiteID=AT
Land's End	https://www.landsend.com/
Target	https://www.target.com

COMPREHENSIVE INFO & SUPPORT

Organization	Website
American Cancer Society	https://www.cancer.org/
Breast Cancer	https://www.breastcancer.org/
CancerCare	https://www.cancercare.org/
Living Beyond Breast Cancer (LBBC)	https://www.lbbc.org/
Susan G. Komen	https://www.komen.org/
Touch–The Black Breast Cancer Alliance™* (BBCA)	https://www.touchbbca.org
Young Survival Coalition*	https://www.youngsurvival.org/

*Special interest focus

CLOTHING

Because...
They co-design their bras and clothes with breast cancer survivors to feel like the hugs we all need. I especially love the zephyr fabric that skims the body just right.
Because their stylish bathing suits with prosthetic pockets look terrific with or without inserts. Of course, I wear mine without prosthetics!
Go Target! They're selling swimsuits and bras for women with mastectomies. They appear as if they'll fit more naturally with prosthetics but still optional.

COMPREHENSIVE INFO & SUPPORT

Because...
They're all about cancer and helping everyone in all kinds of ways.
They talk about going flat and care about the caregivers! Their online community offers clear information and empathy at diagnosis, through treatment, and during whatever comes next.
We all need resources and understanding when breast cancer and mastectomies change our realities.
There's never enough emotional, practical, and evidence-based content for those newly diagnosed, in-treatment, post-treatment, and living with metastatic disease.
SGK is one of the best-known, comprehensive, cancer support organizations.
BBCA is driving collaboration and accountability among patients, survivors, advocates, health care professionals, researchers, and pharmaceutical companies to eradicate black breast cancer.
Their 170 local networking groups, vibrant online community, conference, and free guidebooks are dedicated exclusively to young adults with breast cancer and their caregivers.

FINACIAL ASSISTANCE

Company	Website
Alliance in Reconstructive Surgery (AIRS)	https://airsfoundation.org/
The Pink Fund	https://www.thepinkfund.org/

HEALTHCARE & CLINICAL TRIALS

Organization	Website
George Washington University Mammovan	https://www.gwdocs.com
Mayo Clinic	https://www.mayoclinic.org/
National Institutes of Health (NIH)	https://www.cancer.gov/about-cancer/treatment/clinical-trials https://www.nih.gov/health-information/nih-clinical-research-trials-you
Department of Health and Human Services (DHHS) Office for Human Research Protections	www.hhs.gov/About-Research-Participation

FINANCIAL ASSISTANCE

Because...
Reconstruction surgery is expensive, and AIRS and their partner physicians make it possible for women with limited resources.
Because even short-term financial aid during treatment and recovery helps meet basic needs, decreases stress levels, and allows breast cancer patients in active treatment to focus on healing while improving outcomes.

HEALTHCARE & CLINICAL TRIALS

Because...
This is a super resource in the Washington, DC area. Go to the website, click "specialties," then "mammovan."
They're one of the largest not-for-profit, academic health systems in the country combining clinical practice, education, and research.
Patients and caregivers need reliable information about clinical trials.
Making informed decisions about clinical trials is crucial.

MEDIA

Company	Website
Why Did I Get Cancer Podcast	https://whydidigetcancer.com/
Wildfire Magazine	https://www.wildfirecommunity.org/

RESEARCH

Company	Website
Breast Cancer Research Foundation	https://www.bcrf.org
Metavivor	https://metavivor.org/

SUPPORT

Company	Website
Imerman Angels	https://imermanangels.org/
The Smith Center for Healing and the Arts	https://smithcenter.org/

MEDIA

Because...
A digital space for telling and sharing cancer stories, including interviews about protection with cancer experts.
Wildfire says they're the "only magazine and writing community for the women *too young* for breast cancer."

RESEARCH

Because...
They're one of my favorites, concentrating on preventing and curing breast cancer by supporting the most promising research.
100% of donations support Stage 4 metastatic breast cancer research and they're the only US organization awarding annual Stage 4 breast cancer research funding.

SUPPORT

Because...
This is a caring, one-on-one cancer support community
For people in the Washington, DC area, "The Smith Center for Healing and the Arts offers a diverse range of events and support."

Acknowledgments

When I told my family and friends that my book was going to be published, the unanimous response was,

"You wrote a book?"

It was the last thing anyone, including myself, thought I would do.

With that in mind, I would like to first acknowledge "The Michaels" who got me into this: Michael Sussman, my former DC landlord and current friend, the consummate connector who introduced me to my publisher and mentor, Michael Vezo. From a casual meeting, where I mentioned under my breath that I had scribbled a book, to actually publishing a paper-and-ink volume of my words, this has been one of the most incredible experiences I have ever had. Michael V. taught me a valuable lesson in life with his philosophy, *Never say no to an opportunity.*

Michael V. introduced me to Melonie Mallon and J. McCrary, my editors and guides on my soul-searching journey. With the gentleness and firmness of parents, they took a self-proclaimed nonwriter and transformed me into a person who now loves producing the written word. They are truly miracle workers.

My family and friends have been essential in writing this story. My parents gave me the confidence to do anything and the opportunity to accomplish it. Alan brought me adventure and love, two wonderful daughters, and some of the best memories of my life. My children, their families, and my friends encourage, support, and love me in my life and in this process, and they are my cheering squad and invaluable critics. They push me to dig deep, beyond my limits, and challenge me to not accept just "good enough." They remind me to be honest, give up control, and let it happen. Plus, they give me great material to write about.

Their support gives me the confidence to pursue my obsessions and help me to believe I am okay.

Thank you all.

49248868R00142